THE GAMES

MARJORIE JACKSON PARKWAY
SYDNEY SHOWGROUND
BENNELONG ROAD
Bryan
Is this the Lacrosse Centre???
THE
ROSE AVE
MURRAY
DAWN FRASER AVE
HERB ELLIOTT AVE
AUSTRALIA AVE
Australia Centre
Where's the diving poo
Bicentennial Park
Warm Up Arena
Golf Driving Range
SHIRLEY STRICKLAND AVE
Tennis Centre
Hockey Centre

GAMES

John Clarke *&* **Ross Stevenson**

ABC
BOOKS

Published by ABC Books for the
AUSTRALIAN BROADCASTING CORPORATION
GPO Box 9994 Sydney 2001

First published in November 1999

National Library of Australia
Cataloguing-in-Publication entry

Clarke, John. 1948–.
The games.
ISBN 0 7333 0799 X.
1. Olympic Games (27th: 2000: Sydney, NSW).
2. Olympics – Humor. 3. Sports – Humor.
I. Stevenson, Ross. II. Australian Broadcasting Corporation.
III. Title.
798.480207

Designed by Ruth Grüner
Set in 9.5 pt Frutiger Light by Ruth Grüner
Printed in Australia by Australian Print Group, Maryborough

5 4 3 2 1

CONTENTS

BLAH
BLAH
BLAH Subject: Re: Book Introduction

>From jclarke@thegames.com.au Thu Sep 16 10:02:16 1999
From "John Clarke" <jclarke@thegames.com.au>
To: "Gina Riley" <griley@thegames.com.au>
Subject: Re: Book Introduction
Date: Thu, 16 Sep 1999 10:03:16 + 1000
MIME-Version 1.0
X-MSMail-Priority: High

----- Original Message -----
From: John Clarke <jclarke@thegames.com.au>
Sent: Thursday, 16 September 1999 10:02:16
Subject: Book Introduction

>Gina,
>I've been asked to write an Introduction for some book about the Games.
>Do you know anything about this? Perhaps you could put something together.
>John
>
>

From: griley@thegames.com.au[SMTP:griley@thegames.com.au]
Sent: Thursday, 16 September 1999 10:05:19
To: John Clarke
Subject: Re: Book Introduction

John,
Never heard of it. G.

From: jclarke@thegames.com.au[SMTP:jclarke@thegames.com.au]
Sent: Thursday, 16 September 1999 10:13:43
To: Gina Riley
Subject: Re: Book Introduction

Gina,
I haven't got time to do this. I've got six marching teams in the car park and
Alan Jones is redesigning the Opening Ceremony. I've got him down to three
days but Ric won't wear it and the Minister is in Switzerland until the 19th.
John

From: bdawe@thegames.com.au[SMTP:bdawe@thegames.com.au]
Sent: Thursday, 16 September 1999 10:51:29
To: John Clarke
Subject: Re: Book Introduction

John,
Gina just rang from the Basketball Centre and can you check the Match
Schedule on her computer. It should say 12th-19th. The Official Programme
says 14th-22nd and apparently on the tickets it says October.
Bryan

From: jclarke@thegames.com.au[SMTP:jclarke@thegames.com.au]
Sent: Thursday, 16 September 1999 12:19:56
To: Bryan Dawe
Subject: Re: Book Introduction

Bryan,
Can you put something together that might serve as an Intro to a book?
'Great challenge but very exciting' might be the line to take. Mention the
millennium. Leave it on my desk. I'll have a look at it later. I'm with Nicholas
till 3 and then the reception for some Macedonian Cyclists at Pymble.
John

From: bdawe@thegames.com.au[SMTP:bdawe@thegames.com.au]
Sent: Thursday, 16 September 1999 15:12:11
To: John Clarke
Subject: Re: Book Introduction

John,
I got your message but I'm at Darling Harbour. Television want to put
camera-towers along the foreshore for the Triathalon. Not looking good
for ribbon of historic plants in offending area. I'll be back by about 6.

From: jclarke@thegames.com.au[SMTP:jclarke@thegames.com.au]
Sent: Thursday, 16 September 1999 15:21:24
To: TAB
Subject:

Dave.
Warwick Farm. Race 4. Horse 6. 20 units. Win.
John

From: jclarke@thegames.com.au[SMTP:jclarke@thegames.com.au]
Sent: Thursday, 16 September 1999 17:45:02
To: Gina Riley
Subject: Re: Book Introduction

Gina,
Can you please call me about this book intro?
John

From: griley@thegames.com.au[SMTP:griley@thegames.com.au]
Sent: Thursday, 16 September 1999 18:05:30
To: John Clarke
Subject: Re: Book Introduction

John,
Sure. Turn your phone on. G.

THE PRESS CONFERENCE

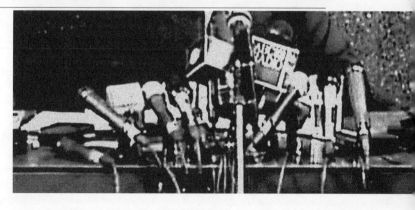

IN A REMARKABLE NEW TYPE OF TELEVISION documentary, the Logistics and Liaison Team for the Year 2000 Olympic Games in Sydney, Australia, was filmed throughout the crucial development and build-up period as the event of the millennium approached. The television crew followed the discussions and filmed developments as they actually occurred. No censorship provision was negotiated and the following transcripts represent a unique record of these important events.

On some occasions the programs went to air preceded by short formal interviews given to the documentary crew earlier in the same week.

John at desk.

JOHN ꞁ It's a huge undertaking, yes, no question about that. And it will be very exciting. I suppose the magnitude of it though . . . I would have expected when I took the job on — it changes all the time. Sorry? No. Well yes, but not now. Okay, sorry. It changes all the time. I mean it stays the same and yet it constantly changes so it's a pretty interesting job and, of course, it is the Olympics. I mean, it doesn't really get any bigger. This is the main event.

Gina at desk.

GINA ꞁ The best experience you can have for doing this job is to actually be doing it. I've had two days off since I started. Sometimes I look out there and think, you know, a day at the beach would be nice. It's just not an option. Not at the moment. It will be. Just not at the moment.

Bryan at desk.

BRYAN ꞁ Well, the job has changed, really. Before, if a problem came up you just had to try to find a way of fixing it. Now, as everybody probably knows, there are budgetary and cash-flow problems. We can't always do exactly what we want to do.

JOHN ꞁ I suppose the difficult time — the most difficult time — probably the next few months. Actually probably the next year. Or the whole period now probably between here and the opening ceremony is a very big time, I think, not just for us — I think it's a very big time for Australia The whole world is watching. It's a very important time. And I hope we get there.

INTERVIEWER ꞁ What's the biggest problem you've got at the moment?

JOHN ꞁ Biggest problem? I suppose I wish we were a bit surer about the budget.

BRYAN ꞁ Yes. It's big business. If the Olympics were listed on the Exchange, it would be Australia's fourth biggest company.

GINA ꞁ We'll get there. Yes. I mean, of course we'll get there. This is not a rehearsal. *(Gina's interview is interrupted as John enters. To John)* What's up?

JOHN ι You wouldn't believe it. You would not bloody well believe it. Oh Christ, you're still filming. I'm sorry about that. Sorry about this. Some guy has got a grant from some minister — small business or something — to go round hotels — Olympic accommodation places — and show people native Australian animals.

GINA ι Live animals?

JOHN ι Yes. Minister thought it was a great idea. Thousands of visitors, far too busy to go out to the bush and see these exquisite creatures bouncing about in the privacy of their continent, so you know, pop down to the foyer . . . see a marsupial.

GINA ι Well, they can't be going to the zoo.

JOHN ι Oh no. The people can't be going to the zoo. Far too important, far too busy. Haven't got the time.

GINA ι So what's the problem?

JOHN ι Well, a slight problem with trials this morning apparently. As a consequence of which apparently seventeen wallabies have got loose in the Hyatt.

GINA ι Where are they now?

Phone rings.

JOHN ι Nobody knows where they are. It's got nothing to do with us, I'm happy to say. If that's for me I'm not here.

Gina answers the phone.

GINA ι Hello. He's not here at the moment. Can I take a message? Yes. Seventeen wallabies, really? Have you tried the Minister's office? I'd try there. Bye.

Bryan enters.

BRYAN ι Turn up the radio.

JOHN ι What's on the radio? This'll be good.

RADIO VOICEOVER ι Anybody who finds one of these wallabies . . . is asked to please contact the Wallaby Hotline on 13 24 87 92. And the forecast today, fine and mild . . .

JOHN ι How about that? They've got a Wallaby Hotline. I don't think even we could have thought of that.

GINA ၊ Oh fantastic.

JOHN ၊ I'll be back here at about quarter to twelve . . .

Later, the three-person Logistics and Liaison Team enters a press conference and sits down.

JOHN ၊ Okay. Now first of all, I'd like to thank you all for coming. It's great to see so many of you here today from such a wide range of media organisations and obviously from so many different countries. That's fantastic for us. And for those of you not from here, we'd like to welcome you to Australia, to our country. I don't know whether we might need an interpreter for those of you. I hope many of you do speak English because we in Australia speak a language we are told is very like English and that will enable you to perhaps grasp aspects of what we are saying.

A journalist asks a question in a foreign language.

JOHN ၊ Ah . . . I beg your pardon? Would you like an interpreter? *(To Gina)* Do you know what's being said there?

GINA ၊ No. Not language I know.

JOHN ၊ I'm sorry, we don't fully understand exactly what you're saying. Does anyone else understand what's being said there? Does anyone else speak this language or a common language — a third language perhaps, which is common to someone else in the room and to our friend here and who could perhaps explain?

GINA ı Look, perhaps if we just try and speak slowly.

BRYAN ı Yes. That's a good idea.

JOHN ı That's not a language you know?

GINA ı No.

JOHN ı I thought you . . .You speak a few languages don't you?

GINA ı Well, yes I do, but not that particular one. Look, I think somebody's trying to do something.

JOHN *(Addressing the full press conference again)* ı Okay. Well, look, welcome anyway. I mean you'll see a lot of cameras here today, a lot of microphones, a lot of radio journalism, a lot of equipment. There are people here from . . . how many countries, Bryan?

BRYAN ı No idea.

JOHN ı Good. There are people here from many different countries . . .

BRYAN ı Lots. Lots of countries.

JOHN ı Lots of countries. Lots of countries, yes. We're very excited about this. Aside from anything else these proceedings are being broadcast live by satellite, which is not something I understand but my kids tell me is 'way cool'. So that's clearly something greatly to be desired. So if anybody is out there watching, welcome. And now I think perhaps I should just say a couple of things about the protocol and the way we would like to conduct the proceedings and then we can take any questions that you might have.

Within hours of the media conference going to air, respected television journalist, Barrie Cassidy, was called in to advise the team on its performance. Barrie is filmed arriving and entering the lift for his meeting with the team.

BARRIE ı Who are you guys?

INTERVIEWER ı Oh, we're making a doco for the ABC.

BARRIE ı Have you cleared it with the Minister?

INTERVIEWER ǀ Yes. It's all official. Are you here because of the press conference?

BARRIE ǀ Yes. I heard it was a bit of a disaster. I got a call from the Minister and they just wanted someone to come around and talk to them. See if we can pick up some lessons for next time maybe. You don't want the public face of the whole operation not working.

INTERVIEWER ǀ What are you going to do with them?

BARRIE ǀ I don't know really, until I've had a look at the tape.

INTERVIEWER ǀ Have you heard it's pretty bad?

BARRIE ǀ I'm sure we'll work something out.

The team has only just learnt that a media consultant is coming in to assess their performance at the press conference.

BRYAN ǀ I think it will be good having someone come in. I mean, it will be interesting. This is not something that we've ever done before and I think there are certain sorts of skills that in some cases we don't have. I think we need back-up.

GINA ǀ I think it's ridiculous. It doesn't address the problem. The problem isn't that we got into a bit of trouble and we need to be taught how to handle a press conference. The problem is we shouldn't have been there in the first place. The Minister should do the press conference.

JOHN ǀ Okay. Are you ready? Now, this is about the media consultant company? Okay. *(John is interrupted when he is preparing his response. A news flash is handed to him.)* Le giardia. What's le giardia? Le giardia Look, I can't . . . We can't drink the water? I can't deal with this at the moment. I've got to do an interview. Actually, hang on. I'd better not do the interview first. I'd better look after the water system. We can drink the water?

Later, the team sits with respected media consultant Barrie Cassidy, watching a replay of their press conference.

JOHN *(Voice on television)* ǀ Now, as you know, we are currently about two and a half years out from the opening ceremony at the Sydney Olympics and we're here today obviously to put you in mind of what we're up to, how we think we're going, how the preparations are coming along.

     We've been working with people right across the entire Games infrastructure in the Government area, in corporate, in the various sporting bodies that are affiliated and in many of the countries who will be here as competitors. We'll obviously be continuing to liaise with these people over the next 27 months. Our job — the job of this group — is to get these games on. We obviously want these games to be, I suppose, one of the greatest sporting festivals that the world's ever seen.

BARRIE ı This is good.

JOHN *(On television screen)* ı And obviously to showcase this wonderful city . . . this fabulous country of ours. Now, I think that's probably enough from me. There are one or two things perhaps we should say and then I think we can get on with any issues you might wish to raise.

BRYAN ı John. Do you want to talk about the venues?

JOHN ı The venues?

BRYAN ı The venues. Yes.

JOHN ı Yes sure. Why do you want to talk about the venues?

BRYAN ı Well, a lot of the facilities are going to be ready early next year and they may like to go out and visit.

JOHN ı Yes, I thought perhaps we might deal with that when we're taking questions but . . .

BRYAN ı Oh, fair enough.

JOHN ı But we could do that. I just wanted to say a couple of things about the media protocol.

GINA ı I think you could start with the venues. That would be good. They want to know about that sort of stuff.

Later, the media consultant analyses the perfomance.

BARRIE ı This is all a bit slow this bit, isn't it?

BRYAN ı Yes, it is.

JOHN ı What do you mean it is? This is your idea, this venue stuff. You did this.

BARRIE ı Does it feel slow to you?

JOHN ı Well it doesn't feel fast.

BARRIE ∣ It's a bit slow.

GINA ∣ It gets fast.

JOHN ∣ It gets a hell of a lot faster in a minute.

On cue, John hits his straps at the press conference.

JOHN ∣ Now, the next few months in Sydney we'll be hosting a fair old welter of international and world-class events. We'll be holding those at the venues that they'll be using for those events at the 2000 Olympics and we will then be consulting with those affiliate bodies about the performance of those venues subsequently and we will be assessing their performance. In the next couple of months in Sydney we will be having international and world-class events in the right venues in, from memory, swimming . . .

BRYAN ∣ Athletics.

JOHN ∣ Athletics.

BRYAN ∣ Judo.

JOHN ι Judo, canoeing, shooting, lacrosse, weight-lifting.

BRYAN ι Soccer.

JOHN ι And soccer. So you will be able to assess those venues.

A journalist interrupts.

JOURNALIST ι Is lacrosse an Olympic sport?

JOHN *(Looks around)* ι I beg your pardon? It must be. I mean they're holding . . . Yes, there's an Olympic Lacrosse Centre and in fact they're holding the, I think, elimination rounds of the East Asian sub-regional section of the current and impending world championships at the Olympic Lacrosse Centre pretty soon and the Olympic Lacrosse Centre of course is in . . .

BRYAN ι It's in Epping, John.

JOHN ι In Epping. In Epping.

JOURNALIST ι Is lacrosse actually an Olympic sport?

JOHN ι Well, I think you can assume from the construction of the Olympic Lacrosse Centre, that yes, lacrosse is an Olympic sport. That's what the venue has been constructed for.

Later, the media analysis continues.

BARRIE ι You're not going anywhere here.

JOHN ι Well, where should I be going?

BARRIE ι You've got to grab the thing back.

The press conference does seem to have bogged down at this point.

JOHN ι Have I seen the Lacrosse Centre? No. I'll be brutally honest with you. I have not seen the Lacrosse Centre itself.

John feels there wasn't much he could have done about it.

JOHN ι Well, we just got besieged with questions at this time.

BARRIE ι You don't have to answer them all.

The media consultant watches as the team gets into further difficulty.

INTERVIEWER ı Who are the current Olympic lacrosse champions?

JOHN ı The current Olympic lacrosse champions? That is not something I would know.

The media consultant addresses the issue.

BARRIE ı The question is not the important thing in these things. The answer is the important thing. You're out there to sell a message — sole purpose. It doesn't matter what the question is, turn it into the answer that you want to give.

This is not exactly what the team did at the press conference.

INTERVIEWER ı Well, why is it not on the official list?

JOHN ı Is it not on the official list? I don't understand quite . . .

GINA ı We'll look into that.

JOHN ı . . . why it wouldn't be on the official list but again we could certainly look into that and get back to you. *(To Bryan)* Get his name.

BRYAN ı I got it.

JOHN ı Right, now you should all have a copy of this. There should have been one on your seat. This is the official handbook. There's information in here about the various sporting programmes, about how we're going. About the construction programmes, about the development of the venues.

Later, in the office, John is pleased to see the press conference get back on the rails. He feels the storm is over.

JOHN ı Anyone want a cup of tea?

GINA ı Ooh, I'd love one. Just a plain tea.

JOHN ı Plain tea.

BRYAN ı Coffee, thanks.

JOHN ı Coffee.

GINA ı And a biscuit.

JOHN ⏐ I don't know if there are any biscuits. Are there any biscuits?

GINA ⏐ Well, there were some before. I bought some. There were chocolate biscuits.

BARRIE *(Not impressed)* ⏐ Do you want to concentrate?

JOHN ⏐ Pardon?

BRYAN ⏐ Sorry?

BARRIE ⏐ Well, this might be part of the problem, mightn't it?

BRYAN ⏐ What is?

BARRIE ⏐ You've got to concentrate.

BRYAN ⏐ Oh, yes, sure.

JOHN ⏐ What are you saying might be part of the problem though?

The media consultant is back looking at the press conference.

JOHN ⏐ In fact we had the head of the IBBF out here this week and he was looking at some of these venues and I don't suppose I'm speaking out of turn in saying that he was absolutely delighted. He said that if they had anything like these venues in Europe they'd be beating them back with a stick. So that's not a bad recommendation. That information is all in here *(Holds up the brochure)* and there's information in there about us. I'll explain a little bit about who we are in a minute, but it's all here as well. Okay?

FEMALE JOURNALIST ı Can I ask a question?

The media consultant wonders if this is the same journalist who was asking about lacrosse.

BARRIE ı Is that the same guy?

BRYAN ı No. different guy.

JOHN ı This guy is a woman, Barrie.

Regardless of whom the journalist is, the question seems to present a difficulty.

JOHN ı The IBBF? The IBBF is the IBBF. The IBBF is . . . I don't know quite who the IBBF is. The head of the IBBF, though, was very, very impressed when I was happy enough to spend some time with him, personally.

BRYAN ı Extremely . . .

JOHN ı Extremely impressed, I think, was the expression he used . . .

FEMALE JOURNALIST ı With what?

JOHN ı With the venue that the discipline managed by the IBBF would be using.

FEMALE JOURNALIST ı What venue is the IBBF using?

The media consultant feels the press conference beginning to drift again.

BARRIE ı You should be back on the agenda here. You've really got to drive the agenda.

At the press conference, the team obviously felt the same.

JOHN ı I'm not absolutely sure but look, I think we're getting a little bit off the agenda here.

FEMALE JOURNALIST ı You don't know?

JOHN ı Well, look, I'm not aware of every aspect of every thing about the literally thousands of events we're going to be running in Sydney 2000 in the hundreds and hundreds of sports. I'll be brutally francis with you; no, I don't know.

The media consultant spots something.

BARRIE ı See that thing you're doing with your hands?

JOHN ı Yes.

BARRIE ı Never do that.

JOHN ı No?

BARRIE ı No. You look shifty. You want people to trust you. You want them to think, 'now here's a guy with all the answers. Here's the guy. I'll listen to him'.

The press conference continues.

JOHN ı For example, when we finish here I have a message here to call somebody from the IWPA. Now, for example, what on earth is the IWPA? Are they the International Water Polo Association? Or the Indian Women's Pentathletes Academy? The International Wilderness Protection Awards? Is it the International Weightlifting Philanthropists of the Argentine?

The media consultant shakes his head.

BARRIE ı This is just a huge distraction isn't it?

GINA ı Pardon?

BARRIE ı This is just a huge distraction.

BRYAN ı Pardon?

JOHN ı Pardon?

GINA ı Pardon?

BRYAN ı Isn't this whole issue just a distraction?

JOHN ı Sorry, Barrie? Yes, it probably was.

Nevertheless, the matter continued to interest the press conference.

JOURNALIST ı So what is the IWPA?

JOHN ı What is it? I think in that case it is the Institute for Women's Polevaulting Accreditation but you can see my point is that there are so many of these small infrastructure organisations, it's terribly hard to keep an actual focus on the individual one.

ANOTHER JOURNALIST ı A lacrosse organisation, perhaps?

JOHN ı No, I don't think it's a lacrosse organisation, no.

FEMALE JOURNALIST ı Is this word on the bottom of page 17 right?

JOHN ı Page 17? You're reading from the Official Handbook? Seventeen — no, that looks like a mistake.

FEMALE JOURNALIST ı What should it be?

JOHN ı Gina?

GINA ı Youth in Asia, I would take it as.

JOHN ı Possibly 'Youth in Asia'. *(He reads it quickly to check it in context)* 'We are particularly pleased with the opportunity this great sporting event affords to appeal to "Euthanasia".' Yes, that should obviously be 'Youth in Asia'. That's a slight mistake. It's in the Regional Development Section so that's probably what it is — 'Youth in Asia'.

FEMALE JOURNALIST ı And the top of page 18?

JOHN ı The year 2000.

FEMALE JOURNALIST ı It says the year 20,000.

JOHN ı I realise it says the year 20,000 but it is obviously supposed to be the year 2000.

BRYAN ı They've just stuck an extra zero in there obviously.

GINA ı It's the year 200 on page 14.

JOHN ı Good God.

JOURNALIST ı No mention of lacrosse?

JOHN ı No, no mention of lacrosse whatsoever. In fact I see no immediate evidence of any mention of lacrosse in the entire handbook since you mention it.

The media consultant has seen enough.

BARRIE ı You see? I think you should grab the initiative here and say, 'Righto. No more questions'. It's time to rein this whole thing in. We're here to talk about whatever.

JOHN ı Yes, well, I agree in principle. I mean, that's all very well but you ought to have a look at this handbook. Everyone in the room has a copy of this handbook. This handbook went out to every media organisation on Earth.

BARRIE ı That's not the point, though.

JOHN ı Well, it's a bit hard to get to the point when everyone's got a copy of a handbook that's full of cock-ups.

The press conference seems to confirm this view.

JOURNALIST ı Can I just check the spelling of 'Sydney' with you?

JOHN ı Certainly. S-Y-D-N-E-Y.

FEMALE JOURNALIST ı The top of page 19 isn't right either.

BRYAN ı Nineteen. *(He looks for it)*

JOHN ı No, that's not, strictly speaking, correct.

GINA ı It's just a little bit wrong.

JOHN ı Yes, it's only slightly out.

BRYAN ı It's not that far off.

JOHN ı Syndey 20,000. But we all know what it's supposed to be.

FEMALE JOURNALIST ı It's not right.

JOHN ı It's not right, no. I'm not saying it's right. It's wrong.

BRYAN ı Well get that rectified . . .

JOHN ı But we know what it's supposed to mean and I've noted your question. Now . . .

GINA ı It's Dysney 200 on page 16.

JOHN ı What? Dysney 200?

BRYAN ı Dysney 200.

GINA ı Dysney 200.

JOHN ı That's not terribly good.

Bryan seeks advice from the media consultant.

BRYAN ı Well, what would you have done here, as a matter of interest?

BARRIE ı Well, the handbook's hardly the point is it?

JOHN ı It's *their* point.

BARRIE ı Who the hell cares what their point is? Did they call this press conference? This is supposed to be your press conference. You drive it.

John drives the press conference.

JOHN ı Okay. Question up the back there.

JOURNALIST ı Who are you all?

JOHN ı Who are we? Yes, I suppose . . .

JOURNALIST ı Tell us what you do.

JOHN ı Yes, we can do that. That's a good point. Bryan is in charge of financial planning and the accounts.

The media consultant approves of this firm response.

BARRIE ı Okay, now you're into it.

John hits his stride.

JOHN ı Gina liaises with all the international sporting bodies, marketing, scheduling, talks to the IFA.

GINA *(Correcting him)* ı IAF.

JOHN ı IAF. The IQP and the RJW.

JOURNALIST ı A lacrosse organisation, perhaps?

GINA ı Lacrosse? No, I don't think so.

The media consultant is distressed at the re-emergence of the lacrosse issue.

BARRIE ı Oh no. Not that bloke again. Don't look over there. You know that idiot is sitting over there. Take your next question from over here.

John was just as distressed at the time.

JOHN ı Another question up the back there.

JOURNALIST ı No dealings with them?

JOHN ı No dealings with lacrosse whatsoever.

BRYAN ı At any time.

JOHN ı At any time. In the past, in the present or in the future. Has anybody got any questions that don't have anything to do with lacrosse?

JOURNALIST ı How much over budget are the games at the moment?

JOHN ı Have we got any more lacrosse questions?

BRYAN *(Interrupts)* ı No, I can answer that John. About $170 million.

JOHN ı At the most.

GINA ı That's the outside isn't it?

BRYAN ı Very outside. Very outside.

FEMALE JOURNALIST ı How many extra people will be in Sydney during the Games?

GINA ı The estimate is about 100,000 athletes and officials and then of course there are the spectators.

The media consultant offers an opinion.

BARRIE ı A lot of people will leave too, of course.

JOHN ı Leave? Why would anybody leave?

BARRIE ı Well, seven people in my street have rented their houses out. They're going.

GINA ı Where are they going?

BARRIE ı They're going to Europe.

BRYAN ı Really?

BARRIE | Yes. They reckon they'll be able to fly there for about 500 bucks.

JOHN | Yes, but you'd want to be here, wouldn't you?

BARRIE | Well, it's going to cost a grand for a cup of coffee here. Tourists want the cheap deal. They're not going to come.

GINA | I thought this was going to bring billions of tourist dollars to Australia.

JOHN | Yes it is. It is. It is. It is.

BARRIE | In Atlanta, a lot more left than arrived.

BRYAN | Really?

JOHN | Really?

The press have one or two outstanding matters of concern.

JOURNALIST | Is Mr Costellopto going to be coming?

JOHN | Mr Who? Mr Costellopto? That's not a name I know. No, whoever he is, I don't think he'll be in attendance. He's certainly not to my knowledge a member of our organisation.

JOURNALIST | He's on the bottom of page 21 . . . Mr Costellopto.

BRYAN | Mr Costellopto.

JOHN | Bottom of page 21. Yes. Where? Oh Costellopto.

The media consultant consults his copy of the handbook.

BARRIE | Did anyone show you these before they went out?

GINA | No. They wouldn't show it to us and then they sent it out to every media outlet in the world. Everyone got a copy of that.

JOHN | Our names are in that. Yes, Mr Costellopto is obviously the acting Prime Minister. The Prime Minister is overseas perhaps.

BARRIE | The photos are printed in reverse. They're all around the wrong way.

GINA | Really?

BARRIE | Look at the writing in the background. It's all around the wrong way.

At the press conference, Gina noticed the same thing.

JOHN ı Really?

GINA ı Yes. His name is Peter Costello. They've put his name next to the 'pto'.

JOHN ı They've run the 'pto' on to the end of his name.

GINA ı See, the 'pto' ought to be down here but they've bunged it on the end of his name. Yours sincerely, Peter Costellopto.

JOHN ı Why have they done that?

BRYAN ı Because they're bloody idiots. That's why.

FEMALE JOURNALIST ı You've been criticised for a lack of women in your organisation.

JOHN ı We have been criticised but I don't think that criticism is very reasonable. There are women involved.

BRYAN ı Yes, Cathy Freeman, for example.

JOHN ı No, I think she means in the administration.

GINA ı There are none.

JOHN ı Well, hang on a minute. I mean, a lot of the blokes who work here are married and obviously their wives would take a fairly active interest, I would think.

BRYAN ı A very active interest.

JOURNALIST ı Your budget figures seem to be blown to the shithouse.

JOHN ı That's a question is it, Shakespeare?

The media consultant is absorbed by an earlier problem.

BARRIE ı You do know Peter Costello is not Deputy Prime Minister?

BRYAN ı Sorry?

JOHN ı Isn't he? Who is?

BARRIE ı Tim Fischer.

JOHN ı Oh, what's Peter Costello then?

BARRIE ı Well, he's Deputy Leader of the Liberal Party but he's not Deputy Prime Minister.

GINA ı He *is* in the handbook.

BARRIE ı Can I use the phone?

JOHN ı Yes. On the desk.

Gina, Bryan and John leave.

BARRIE *(On phone)* ı I've been right through it with them. It was a terrible mess. Yes. Everything you were told about it was absolutely right. It was a shambles. But you know, I don't think it was entirely their fault. Did you see this handbook that went out? The one with John's photo on the back? The biggest cock-up I've ever seen. I'd like you to have a look at the video tape as well. Really, they made quite a good fist of it. I doubt whether anybody else would have stayed in the room.

Gina, John and Bryan confront the fact that the press conference wasn't an unbridled success.

BRYAN ı That was a disaster. What did you think?

JOHN ı It wasn't good. Wasn't good.

GINA ı It was a shocker. There's poor Barrie in there trying to say something positive about us.

BRYAN ı It was embarrassing.

JOHN ı Yes, well half the questions were about the bloody handbook. It was a bit hard for us to get the thing off the ground.

BRYAN ı Well, why was the handbook so bad?

GINA ı Because they wouldn't consult with us. They didn't show it to us. I knew they'd stuff up.

JOHN ı How did they get the contract to do the handbook?

GINA ı Aha, I did a little research. Have a look at the names in here. This one, this one and this one.

JOHN ı Remarkable similarity of surname, you'd have to say.

GINA ı Mmmm.

BRYAN ı Are they related?

GINA ı Only a bit.

JOHN ı It's a great country this, isn't it?

BARRIE *(On phone)* ı Page 23. Yes. Picture of Darling Harbour, right? See the list of names on the right — second one. Now go down the page to the committee — second from the bottom. Now look at the partners in the agency. That's the one. That's how they got the contract.

BRYAN ı When are we having another press conference?

JOHN ı I think we've got one at nine o'clock on Wednesday morning.

BRYAN ı What's it about?

JOHN ı About the athletics schedule, I think.

GINA ı It's about all the schedules.

BRYAN ı Can we get a copy of the schedule before that?

GINA ı Yes, yes. It's all under control. It's all done.

JOHN ı Who's got them?

JOHN ı Gina.

GINA ı John.

FUNDING

The three Games supremos have consented to provide brief formal interviews in order to inform the public about how well things are going.

JOHN ǀ I'm just trying to find a well-known athlete to come with me to this thing this evening. I've got to go and address 500 businesspeople and it's always just so much easier if you can go with someone they recognise.

GINA ǀ I suppose we're a bit concerned about ticket sales at the moment not moving as fast as we'd like. I was out talking to the institutions yesterday. We have these corporate packages but I don't quite know what we've got to do.

BRYAN ǀ Oh, I'm sure the corporates will come to the party. Nobody's buying their tickets now, even though they'll get better value. I don't know why. Don't ask me.

JOHN ǀ Well I'm going and try to get them to start taking up these corporate packages. I think they represent very good value. I think they're good for business and it wouldn't do us any harm if we managed to shift a few at this stage.

Tuesday 8.00 a.m. John is coming to work on the bus. He reads the financial pages of the paper and prepares his mind to deal with weighty issues. His deep concentration is broken only slightly by the sounds of other Australians at work.

BUS DRIVER ǀ Get out of the bloody way you idiot! You can't turn right. Read the sign, you clown.

RADIO VOICEOVER ǀ Well, we were wrong about old Richo. After the glowing tribute His Excellency Juan Antonio Samaranch paid to this city and its preparations, I remind you of what he said. Quote: 'I have never seen a Games so advanced'. That's what he said. But it's time to give credit where credit is due and Games insiders tell me that the man who is almost single-handedly responsible for this state of preparedness is Graham Richardson. So to you Richo, my son, and I know you're listening, Albie dips his lid, he says he's sorry, and Albie says 'Well done!'.

RADIO VOICEOVER ǀ This is SFM Sydney. You're with Albert Einstein.

In the office, the wheels of international organisation and protocol are already turning.

BRYAN ǀ Good God! Gina. Did you know that every decision we make has to be run past the Department of Youth and Recreation in order to evaluate its impact on young people?

GINA ǀ Truly?

BRYAN ǀ We are youth obsessed in this country. I mean, the Europeans really value the contribution of their elderly. Juan Antonio Samaranch. What's he? 78? Havalanche — he's 80 and he's in charge of the biggest sport in the world.

GINA ǀ Bowls? *(Bryan sees no merit in this suggestion. Gina reconsiders)* No. No, netball's the biggest sport in the world, isn't it? *(Bryan clearly thinks the biggest sport in the world had wider currency than is indicated by the current discussion)* Fishing? *(Bryan provides a practical demonstration of the sport being played. Gina watches carefully)* Folk dancing? Some sort of rutting ritual?

BRYAN ǀ Soccer. A billion players worldwide.

GINA ǀ Bowls has got that covered, hasn't it?

BRYAN ǀ Eighty years of age. We would have had him kneecapped at forty.

John enters and checks the message machine.

JOHN ǀ Good morning.

GINA ǀ Morning.

JOHN ǀ Morning. Ah, one message! This is the Olympics and we have one message. The rest of the world has conducted its business while we slept and we have one message. Let's hear it, world.

John puts the answering machine on.

JOHN ǀ How can we help you?

FOREIGN VOICE ON MACHINE ǀ So if you could call me back on that number at your earliest convenience Mr Clarke, I would be very grateful.

John addresses the machine.

JOHN ǀ After the beep. After the beep. Apres le bloody beep.

GINA ǀ Maybe the message isn't funny enough.

BRYAN ǀ Yes, you know studies show that people are more inclined to leave a message if they're funny, John.

JOHN ǀ Studies show that a lot of studies are crap, Bryan.

GINA ı Have you been to the toilet today?

JOHN ı You know what irritates me?

GINA ı Pollen?

JOHN ı I'll tell you what irritates me. Have you read the paper this morning?
There are 93 people in there who have been given credit for things we did. There are photographs of them at cocktail parties, sometimes in groups. Can't these idiots in the press get anything right?

GINA ı John, you won't do any publicity.

JOHN ı Why should we do publicity?

GINA ı Because if we don't, these people will quite happily take the credit.

JOHN ı We shouldn't have to do publicity. I'm concerned that the wrong people are getting the credit.

GINA ı Look, I've said before, we just need to do an interview to send out to people, then they can run that and they don't need to get stuff from these other imposters.

JOHN ı You think that *I* should be doing an interview.

GINA ı I do.

JOHN ı Bryan, have you got those figures?

GINA ı We have to do an interview, John.

JOHN ı Yes, right, we'll do that Gina. I've got to go to treasury, Bryan. They'll ask me what they always ask me — 'Are we going to break even like Atlanta?'

BRYAN ı Like what?

JOHN ı Like Atlanta. Atlanta broke even — isn't that the story?

BRYAN ı It's a bit early to tell.

JOHN ı Well, take your time Bryan. There's a whole century not touched yet.

BRYAN ı I'll know when they know.

JOHN ı Atlanta don't know whether they broke even?

BRYAN ı No, it's too hard to tell. The figures haven't all come in yet: 65 per cent of the Atlanta budget was value-in-kind payments.

JOHN ı Value-in-kind payments? What are value-in-kind payments?

BRYAN ı Yes, that's what's hard to tell. It's interpreted in different ways.

JOHN ı How did *they* interpret it? Let's use them as a basis. How did they interpret it?

BRYAN ı It's impossible to know. You'd have to go through all the accounts of all the companies concerned.

JOHN ı No, Bryan. No. Look, you've got your expenses down one side and your income down another side and they balance. Isn't that the way it works?

BRYAN ı I know that's the theory and I would have thought so too, but things change. For example, do you realise that our budget has risen by 50 per cent?

JOHN ı Our budget?

BRYAN ı Since we got the right to stage this thing.

JOHN ı Fifty per cent up?

BRYAN ı Yes.

JOHN ı That's not terribly good, is it?

BRYAN ǀ Well it's all right if income has risen by 50 per cent.

JOHN ǀ Can I ask you a personal question?

BRYAN ǀ Yes.

JOHN ǀ Has income risen by 50 per cent?

BRYAN ǀ I doubt it.

JOHN ǀ You doubt it? You don't know, Bryan? I thought you did this for a living.

BRYAN ǀ John, the income isn't in yet, okay? Sometimes it doesn't come in early. Most times it doesn't come in till afterwards. It's really, really tricky.

JOHN ǀ Bryan, I tell you what, the public are not going to wear a shortfall on the Games. I'll tell you that now.

BRYAN ǀ Yes but John, there are certain monies that we only have a provision for, for a start.

JOHN ǀ A provision for?

BRYAN ǀ Yes.

JOHN ǀ As distinct from what?

BRYAN ǀ Like, an amount.

JOHN ǀ I'd like forty dollars worth of petrol. I haven't got any money but I've made a provision for it.

BRYAN ǀ Hang on. I'll give you an example. Take the Olympic Stadium, right? Would you say the Olympic Stadium is an expense of the Games?

JOHN ǀ Obviously it's an expense of the Games.

BRYAN ǀ Of course it is. Okay. Now, the Olympics will last two weeks but the Olympic Stadium — that's going to be there for a long time.

JOHN ǀ What are you going to regard it as if you don't regard it as an expense of the Olympics? It's an Olympic Stadium.

BRYAN ǀ John, will you please trust me? All right? *(Bryan prepares to leave)* Sydney will break even. I've got to go. I'm sorry.

John considers what he has just been told.

JOHN ∣ We're 50 per cent over and Sydney will break even. *(To Gina)* He's a bit casual isn't he? I mean he's just told me that the Sydney Games are going to break even, having previously told me we're 50 per cent over budget.

GINA ∣ I've been saying for ages we should be looking at our costs.

Bryan is travelling in the back of a car. He is a thoughtful and generous person.

BRYAN ∣ The thing about John and Gina is — and they're really good at what they do — is they don't understand finance. They just don't have an instinct for it. I could spend the whole day explaining a funding problem to John. It's just easier for me to come out here and fix it. I am going right now to a meeting with a potential sponsor of the Games and this is potentially an extremely lucrative deal. *(He speaks to the television crew)* Okay, you guys will have to stay here, I'm afraid. Wish me luck.

Bryan is dropped off and the camera crew doubles back and is returning to the office when Bryan comes out the back of the building and walks briskly across a street and into another office-tower.

CAMERA OPERATOR ∣ Look! There's Bryan. What's he doing coming out of the back of the building? I wonder where he's going. I wonder what he's doing.

Tuesday 8.57 a.m. John is reading the newspaper. He is sufficiently engaged by what he reads, to actually talk to the pages.

JOHN ∣ That's not right. That's wrong. That's not that guy's position. He is not the head of the Athletics Federation. Sorry, he isn't. That is completely wrong. Check your facts. He's not Portuguese, he's Polish. And you sir, are a bloody idiot.

Tuesday 9.40 a.m. John and Gina have been called to a meeting with the Minister's Secretary at an advertising agency.

GINA ∣ Does it matter who gets the credit as long as it happens?

JOHN ∣ No, not in the least. What matters is who doesn't get the credit. You don't want the wrong people getting the credit. Did you hear that bonehead from the Shire of Complete Galah on TV this morning explaining how he — he, personally — had convinced the Minister to run the cycling race through the picturesque hamlet of Lookatmydick.

GINA ı Yes. We had to talk him into it.

JOHN ı All his idea, according to the telly.

GINA ı As I said, I'll arrange an interview, and we'll supply it to the media.

JOHN ı I think that's a good idea.

GINA ı Really? When are you available?

JOHN ı No, *I'm* not doing an interview.

GINA ı Oh, make up your mind John.

JOHN ı Incidentally, if Bryan's right, we're going to have to take a serious look at our costs.

Nicholas, Secretary to the Minister, walks into the room with Kid Curry, a young person skilled in advertising and marketing.

NICHOLAS ı Morning.

JOHN ı Morning.

NICHOLAS ı Is the Minister here yet?

KID CURRY ı The Minister phoned. He's out at the stadium.

JOHN ı Ah, well . . .

KID CURRY ı A truck turned over at Stanmore.

JOHN ı Ah well, he'll be all day.

KID CURRY ı He actually said to go ahead without him. He asked if *you* were here, though.

NICHOLAS ı Is anyone from SOCOG coming?

KID CURRY ı There were supposed to be two SOCOG people coming. Mr Coates rang to see if Mr Gosper was here because he's stuck up at Pymble and can't get here in time and Mr Gosper rang just before you arrived to say he's on the bridge and will have to go straight to his 10 o'clock.

NICHOLAS ı What about Glenda and Igor? Are they coming?

KID CURRY ı Haven't heard from them. They're coming from Windsor. You never know what time they're going to get here.

NICHOLAS ı All right then, we might as well start.

KID CURRY ı That's right.

NICHOLAS ı This is John and Gina. I invited them to come along and have a look because they'll need to be across whatever we're doing in this area.

KID CURRY ı Fine.

GINA ı Hello.

JOHN ı G'day, how are you?

KID CURRY ı Now, the purpose of this was to address the question of how people get around Sydney during the Games. This is where Atlanta was a complete disaster. You had thousands of doves released, you had Muhammad Ali, people in space suits being propelled through the air in mini rockets, laser light shows, Michael Jackson . . .

JOHN ı Athletes.

KID CURRY ı Pardon?

JOHN ı Athletes. There were some athletes in Atlanta, according to the information I got.

KID CURRY ı Yes, sure, there was all sorts of crap. The problem was you couldn't get around the town, right? Nothing worked. What we're trying to do here is snooker the idea that Sydney is a difficult city to get around in. I mean, let's face it: Sydney can be pretty difficult to get around in if you don't know what you're doing.

NICHOLAS ı I'm not sure that's what we should be saying here. Is it?

KID CURRY ı Oh no, it's not what we're saying here. I'm just explaining the problem.

NICHOLAS ı I see.

KID CURRY ı Put it this way: you wouldn't want to have to get from Bondi to Mosman after work, would you?

A moment of confusion occurs in the mind of the Minister's Secretary.

NICHOLAS ı Is he saying it is difficult to get around the city or it isn't?

GINA ı I think he's saying it is, but the purpose of the video is to point out that it isn't.

KID CURRY ı Exactly. I'm saying the video tries to counter the suggestion that Sydney is a difficult city to get around in. That's what we were asked to do.

NICHOLAS | Yes, but you seem to be saying it is difficult to get around the city.

KID CURRY | Yes, that's the problem. In the brief, that was the problem.

NICHOLAS | And the video says the opposite?

KID CURRY | Yes. That's why you wanted the video.

NICHOLAS | All right. Okay. Let's have a look at it then, shall we?

KID CURRY | Right. This video is going out to people who have never even been here. They're not going to know what the place is like.

GINA | They're going to think the city works perfectly well.

KID CURRY | Exactly.

NICHOLAS | Let's see the tape.

A very high-class promotional video of Sydney rolls. It features shots of the harbour, beaches, city buildings, ferries, native flora and fauna.

VIDEO VOICEOVER | Sydney. City of excitement. Sydney. City of sails in the land of opportunity. Capital of Australia's most historic and interesting state. Heart of this young and vibrant nation. Nestled in the greatest harbour in the world and washed by the warm life-giving waters of the South Pacific.

Sydney — host of the 2000 Olympic Games. The home of Australia's greatest sportsmen and equally famed for its nightlife, Sydney is preparing to welcome you into its arms. We hope you have a wonderful time in our city. We think you'll love it. As we say here, 'No wucking furries'.

Here we see the city bustling at lunchtime as businessmen take a break from the pressure of closing that deal, securing that important contract or failing to use privileged information to their own advantage on the stock market.

Water transport is common in the Venice of the south. It's nothing for Mr Robinson to catch a ferry to and from work, using his powerful legs to propel him over the short distances along the city's attractively designed streets. Here we also see the most famous architectural feature in the world — the Sydney Opera House.

Some take their cars, often manufactured by the burgeoning local automotive industry. Here commuters are crossing the Sydney Harbour Bridge. Regal, ain't she?

For those who live further out of town, amongst the gum trees, surrounded by kangaroos and native corroborations, the wide freeways endure smooth and rapid progress with clearly marked exits and entrances. If you like driving, you're going to love this.

In older times Sydney was used as a penal colony. And many convicts first saw this land as their prison ship nudged its way up this magnificent harbour.

Sure, we've changed. Everyone changes who comes here. It'll change you too. No wucking furries.

Tape ends. The Minister's Secretary and the Kid are flushed with pride. Others are more circumspect.

KID CURRY ı Well, what do you think?

NICHOLAS ı I think it's great.

JOHN ı Where's this going?

KID CURRY ı In the media package.

GINA ı What exactly is the media package? Where's it coming from?

NICHOLAS ı This is why I wanted you two here. The Minister wanted to put together a package that could go out to the media in all the countries coming to the Games.

KID CURRY ı It's a postcard.

JOHN ı Who's paying for this?

NICHOLAS ı Well, it will come out of the marketing allocation.

JOHN ı Hang on a minute, why are we paying for this? We haven't got the money to pay for this.

GINA ı We didn't even know it was happening. We're preparing our *own* package to go out to the media.

JOHN ı Are we?

GINA ı Yes.

KID CURRY ı I'll get some coffee.

NICHOLAS ı I think the Minister feels that this is what we need. And you should stop work on yours because this will do the job.

GINA ı Well, what are we going to do with *ours*?

JOHN ı Will you get the Minister to write to me, please, and explain that he has commissioned this, and that he has seen it and that he approves of it and that he is instructing us to pay for it?

NICHOLAS ⏐ Why do you want a letter?

JOHN ⏐ I think if you want us to stop work on ours, I'd like to see that in the form of a letter.

NICHOLAS ⏐ Why do you want a *letter*?

JOHN ⏐ We didn't do this and I would like to see that written down.

NICHOLAS ⏐ Why?

JOHN ⏐ I think you're going to have problems with it, that's why.

NICHOLAS ⏐ What problems?

Kid returns with coffee.

JOHN ⏐ Well, this is not Australia's most historic state. It is not the most interesting. It is not the heart of this young and vibrant nation, which incidentally might be among the oldest countries on the terrestrial crust. It is not the home of Australia's greatest sportsmen. The most famous architectural feature in the world is arguably not the Opera House.

KID CURRY ⏐ That's just in the voiceover.

NICHOLAS ⏐ That's just in the voiceover.

GINA ⏐ Where did you get the shots of the freeway?

KID CURRY ⏐ I don't remember exactly.

GINA ⏐ I do.

NICHOLAS ⏐ Where?

GINA ⏐ That's the road between Brisbane and the Gold Coast. Not even in New South Wales.

NICHOLAS ⏐ Was that the shot of the traffic moving smoothly?

JOHN ⏐ With the very attractive Queensland licence plates. Going like the clappers. There's nothing up there.

KID CURRY ⏐ No-one's going to notice that. It's going to be played in Canada and Zimbabwe.

GINA ⏐ And the shots of the Botanical Gardens?

KID CURRY ⏐ Well, the Botanical Gardens.

GINA ⏐ Which Botanical Gardens?

KID CURRY ⏐ Who cares?

NICHOLAS ⏐ Which Botanical Gardens are they?

JOHN & GINA ⏐ The *Melbourne* Botanical Gardens.

GINA ⏐ Shots of the MCG were beautiful.

JOHN ⏐ Weren't they beautiful?

JOHN ⏐ Just a letter will do. Simple letter. That'll be good.

In another part of the city, Bryan has bumped into the television crew.

CAMERA OPERATOR ⏐ There's Bryan.

BRYAN ⏐ What are you doing here? *(He realises he must explain what he is doing)* They're thinking it over. Fingers crossed.

Tuesday 11.34 a.m. John and Gina are in a car on their way back to the office. Gina is attempting to assemble the elements of a press interview with John.

GINA ı Favourite drink?

There is no answer.

GINA ı Oh come on, it's a simple enough question. John, if you're not going to do any media then don't complain if other people get the coverage. Do you have a favourite sporting memory?

There is no answer.

GINA ı That rules out the *Telegraph Mirror*.

There is no answer.

GINA ı What book changed your life?

There is no answer.

GINA ı Rules out the *Sydney Morning Herald*. What couldn't you do without?

JOHN ı My arse.

GINA ı Rules out the literary pages of the *Australian*. Are you doing up a loft in Bondi?

There is no answer.

GINA ı Rules out the *Good Weekend*. Well, this is going awfully well.

Bryan, in another car, seems pleased with the way his meetings have gone.

BRYAN ı John and Gina will be delighted. Surprised and delighted. This is great news. Twenty-five million.

CAMERA OPERATOR ı What? How much?

BRYAN ı Twenty-five million. Twenty-five million dollars in sponsorship money at this stage will provide enormous budgetary relief. It'll just take the pressure off everyone. I think we've done quite well here.

John and Gina are briefed about Bryan's triumph. There is a pause and then a reaction.

JOHN ｜ Tobacco sponsorship?

BRYAN ｜ Yes. Twenty-five million dollars.

JOHN ｜ Well done, Bryan. That really is terrific news. Now here's a number. *(He writes)* I want to see if you can go and get some more. You ring that. That's the Cambodian Embassy. They'll have a number for the estate of the late Pol Pot. See if you can get them to tip some money into a humanitarian sponsorship of some kind. You seem to be pretty good at it.

BRYAN ｜ Was that an ironical reference?

GINA ｜ Well spotted.

BRYAN ｜ John, it's a legally sold product.

JOHN ｜ Bryan. Not to small children.

BRYAN ｜ John, the Formula One Grand Prix has tobacco sponsorship.

JOHN ｜ That's not a sport.

BRYAN ｜ And that's not an argument.

JOHN ｜ Bryan, the Formula One Grand Prix is currently less interesting than the video game that's based on it. The cars go round in a circle, they get Murray Walker off the ceiling, the race itself is a procession. You can't get past — the car in front at the beginning wins the race. The whole thing is decided by who's going to have a pit stop. They're the fastest cars on earth and the key element, Bryan, is not racing, it's parking.

BRYAN ｜ Okay, forget the Grand Prix. All right? Why do you think they're interested in this, John?

JOHN ｜ I haven't got time to discuss with you the relative merits of tobacco sponsorship but I'll tell you something now Bryan, the Federal Government is not going to wear it.

BRYAN ｜ It was their idea.

JOHN ı Bryan, the Health Minister is a doctor.

BRYAN ı He had to stop being a doctor to become the Health Minister. He can't do both. He's not Superman.

JOHN ı Bryan, I very seldom give an order but the following is an order. Go and tell them 'No'. Go immediately. Do not pass go, do not collect two hundred dollars. God knows what they've done already. They'll have done press releases. It'll be in the evening news. Go now and tell them 'No'.

Some time later, Bryan leaves a city building. He is happy and smiling. He addresses the camera.

BRYAN ı Peace in our time.

Tuesday 1.38 p.m. John and Gina are in the office, engaged in matters of the utmost importance.

GINA ı I'll make it up.

JOHN ı Well, you just do whatever you think is appropriate.

GINA ı Oh, all right then. Your favourite sporting memory is Betty Cuthbert's win in the hundred metres in Melbourne.

JOHN ı I remember it well.

GINA ı Good.

JOHN ı I nearly fell out of my cradle with excitement the day that happened.

GINA ı Your favourite drink . . . apple and guava juice.

JOHN ı Why don't you just put 'wanker'?

Bryan enters.

BRYAN ı Okay, four million dollars. No signage, no advertising, no commercials, no mentions of anything. Okay? That's it.

GINA ı We don't have to do anything?

BRYAN ı Hardly a thing.

GINA ı What is that thing?

BRYAN ı Whenever the three of us are outdoors, at an official outdoor event, in our official capacity, doing what we do at these occasions, the three of us just . . . well, we're required to smoke, that's all.

GINA ı This only applies to official outdoor events.

BRYAN ı Yes, yes, yes.

JOHN ı No compunction to smoke at unofficial indoor events.

BRYAN ı Absolutely none whatsoever.

JOHN ı None whatsoever. Bryan, would I be right in assuming that under this deal you have managed to so cleverly forge, we would be required to hold a number of these official outdoor events?

BRYAN ı I do remember there was some sort of mention of this but only in a general sense.

JOHN ı How many?

BRYAN ı How many of these public events would need to be held outdoors?

JOHN ı Mmm.

BRYAN ı These events at which under this sponsorship arrangement we'd be required to smoke?

JOHN ı I repeat . . . Mmmm.

BRYAN ı John, look, I mean, really, come on, be fair. If the Federated Shoemakers Union offered you four million dollars to put on a pair of their shoes every day, you'd do it, wouldn't you?

JOHN ı Are they coming in here offering me four million dollars to do that?

BRYAN ı John, you smoke.

JOHN ı I haven't touched one in eight years.

GINA *(Perks up at this point and writes enthusiastically)* ı Non-smoker.

BRYAN ı John, smokers don't give up, they just stop for a while. I'm not asking you to smoke for the rest of your life, just for two years. Two years!

JOHN ı No!

BRYAN ı You're just afraid if you start again you won't stop.

JOHN ı Well that's the thing with addictive chemicals, Bryan.

GINA *(Writing again)* ı Anti-drugs.

BRYAN ı John, somewhere in this city in the next five years you'll be going for a jog with your triple A-rated lung capacity and you're going to come across a group of schoolchildren gazing wistfully at a vacant block of land thinking to themselves 'What happened to the school that I was going to go to?' A school that won't be built now because we have a four-million-dollar shortfall in the Games budget because you have no self-control.

JOHN ı Why are you puffing, Bryan?

BRYAN ı I'm not.

JOHN ı Bryan, we've had this discussion. Go and tell them 'No'. That is the end.

BRYAN ı No? Say no?

JOHN ı Yes, do it now.

GINA *(Impressed, writing)* ı Strong willed.

JOHN ı Thanks for your help, Gina.

Tuesday 3.10 a.m. The answering machine spits into life.

JOHN *(Voice on machine)* ı Hi, our answering machine is technically broken. This is the air conditioner. Please leave a message.

BRYAN ı Hi, it's Bryan. I'll be back in ten minutes.

In his office, John is talking on the telephone.

JOHN ı Hello. What star sign am I?
        Gina, that is the worst Irish accent I have ever heard in my life.

Later, Bryan stands in John's office and petitions him.

BRYAN ı John, I tried to tell them 'No' but they refused to talk to me any more. They only want to talk to you. They're sending over their top man now.

JOHN ı Oh God, Bryan. Who is he?

BRYAN ı His name's Fysema. I've never met him but he's their top man from headquarters. Boss cocky. Only talk to you.

JOHN ι I refuse to see him, Bryan.

BRYAN ι John, come on. He's early. You've got to see him.

JOHN ι All right, Bryan. Go and tell him to come in. *(John addresses the camera crew on a matter of protocol)* You'd better go. I'd better tell him the news myself. Thanks. Go on. Off you go!

BRYAN ι Michael Fysema, John Clarke.

JOHN ι Mr Fysema. Sit down, Michael. I think I can probably save you and your organisation a bit of time here. I'm aware that Bryan has been in discussion with you and your colleagues. I'm aware of what's being proposed. We're not in a position to accept your kind offer. Thank you. No one here smokes and neither will anyone smoke. The charter of the Olympics specifically precludes our accepting tobacco sponsorship and even if it didn't, we wouldn't. There are fundamental objections obviously, principally in the area of public health, so our firm answer is 'No' and that will remain the case whatever you have to say. I want that to be crystal clear, thank you.

Mr Fysema has a synthetic voice-box. He places a device on his throat and speaks in a mechanical voice.

FYSEMA ι We have one last offer.

John travelling on a bus. A woman is reading an article about him. She turns and checks that he is the man photographed. He is.

WOMAN ON BUS ı Apple and guava. Wanker!

ROBBO AND THE 100 METRES

EVERY NOW AND AGAIN IN AN EXERCISE OF this complexity, a serious problem emerges, such as an apparent contradiction in the dimensions of a 100-metre track or perhaps a major political figure turning up at a press conference with out-of-date research information and wrongly briefed.

The odds against both these things happening at the same time are astronomical. Australia is fortunate indeed to have a team of dedicated professionals who can step up to situations of this kind and confront them squarely.

John, Gina and Bryan consent to an interview beforehand in John's office.

GINA *(To camera)* ⏐ Yes, the marketing is still a worry. We've got 115 authorised products in the shops but they're just not moving. The mascots are doing well. They're selling like hot cakes, these things. *(She picks up an attractively designed synthetic marsupial)*

CAMERA OPERATOR ⏐ Isn't that good?

GINA ⏐ Yes, it's good but the market they're selling to is the 'Bananas in Pyjamas' market, so basically they're selling to people who don't know what the Olympics are.

JOHN *(To camera)* ⏐ Yes, that is a concern. I think we might have to have a look at our product at some stage.

BRYAN *(To camera)* ⏐ Far and away the greatest response we've had from people buying tickets is for the swimming, perhaps because Australia did very well in the swimming in Atlanta.

JOHN *(To camera)* ⏐ It's hard to know. At the moment, logically, you would have to say we are selling a lot of tickets to people who want to go to the previous Olympics and a great amount of product to people who don't know what the Olympics are.

Wednesday 9.08 a.m. Bryan approaches the receptionist.

BRYAN ⏐ Richard, would you send this to the Minister's office, please?

GINA ⏐ Bryan, what do you make of this?

BRYAN *(Reading)* ⏐ The Iranian Athletics Federation is coming here for a fact-finding mission and they want you to book them twelve hotel rooms.

GINA ⏐ You see?

BRYAN ⏐ See what?

GINA ⏐ Iranians speak Arabic. Arabic is written from right to left. Do they want twelve rooms or twenty-one rooms?

BRYAN ⏐ It's written in English.

GINA ⏐ Yes, the words are in English but I don't know what language the numbers are in.

BRYAN ⏐ When do they arrive?

GINA ɪ January 27th.

BRYAN ɪ Unless, of course, it's January the 72nd.

GINA ɪ Yes. Fair point.

BRYAN ɪ Are you organising Robbo's press conference?

GINA ɪ Yes. In about three seconds.

BRYAN ɪ Best of luck.

John arrives at the office, sweeping through the foyer and greeting his first two appointments as he enters.

JOHN ɪ Oh, good morning. *(To Mr Wilson and Jasmine)* Good morning. Mr Wilson, I gather. Come in. Hello Jasmine. Nice to see you. If you wouldn't mind going down to my office, I'll be with you in a moment.

BRYAN ɪ Good morning.

JOHN ɪ Good morning.

JASMINE ɪ Good morning, Bryan.

BRYAN ɪ Good morning, Jasmine.

John speaks quietly to Bryan.

JOHN ɪ Bryan, *that* is Mr Wilson. Morning, Gina. What are you up to?

GINA ɪ Robbo's doing a press conference at ten.

JOHN ɪ Is there no end to his talents? Have you got it all organised?

GINA ɪ Yes. You're expected there, you know.

JOHN ɪ Oh well, I'll get there as soon as I can. I might be a minute or two. These two could bore for their country.

GINA ɪ His assistant wants some briefing notes.

JOHN ɪ Certainly. What on?

GINA ɪ His speciality today is Environmental Safeguards of the 2000 Olympics.

JOHN *(Gesturing to an item in a pile of research material)* ɪ Look. Yonder brochure contains all the information you will need.

GINA ı Oh thank you. I've got to go.

JOHN ı It's only ten past nine.

GINA ı You know what the traffic is like.

JOHN ı I do. It's a good thing we're not expected to run a major sporting event in this city. It could well be complete mayhem.

GINA ı I'll be back.

JOHN ı I'm sure you will. *(To camera)* We have to speak to Mr Wilson. However, we first have to endure the marketing thoughts of Jasmine Holt. She shares these thoughts with us about once a month and she's from the Federal Government. So just bear with us.

BRYAN *(To camera)* ı Relative of the Minister.

They enter the office where Mr Wilson and Jasmine are waiting for them.

JOHN ı Good morning.

JASMINE ı Good morning.

JOHN *(To the receptionist)* ı No calls, thank you, for five minutes. *(Turns to Mr Wilson)* Mr Wilson.

JASMINE ı Now John . . .

JOHN ı Or Jasmine, of course. That's the other obvious alternative.

JASMINE ı John. I've made a list of a few things I think we ought to be looking at from a corporate relations point of view. I see the Games in the new millennium as a chance to clear out some of the dead wood that we've accumulated over the last century. Some of these things have got a bit of a limp up over the years and I think we could safely wheel them behind the canvas screen for the final round up, if you get my drift.

JOHN ı What sort of things?

JASMINE ı The Olympic Oath.

JOHN ı The Olympic Oath given by the athletes at the start of the Games?

JASMINE ı Yes.

JOHN ı The one written by the founder of the modern Olympics, the one that's been in use for about a thousand years?

JASMINE ꞁ And doesn't it show?

JOHN ꞁ 'I promise to compete in these Olympics for the glory of sport and the honour of the teams.' That one? Noble sentiments, Jasmine.

JASMINE ꞁ Now, the medals.

JOHN ꞁ Gone?

JASMINE ꞁ A bit of a rework.

JOHN ꞁ Ah. Brighter colours perhaps?

JASMINE ꞁ The shape needs work.

JOHN ꞁ Round obviously being . . .

JASMINE ꞁ A cliché.

JOHN ꞁ Of course.

JASMINE ꞁ Now, the Parade of Nations. Greece first, Australia last? Alphabetically it's all over the shop. Needs work. Anyway we'll get back to that one because there's this one. Yes, this one. The traditional release of the doves on their flight of peace. Frankly, I was hoping for something a little more Australian.

JOHN ꞁ Australian?

JASMINE ꞁ Emus, perhaps?

JOHN ꞁ Emus?

JASMINE ꞁ Yes.

BRYAN ꞁ Emus don't fly, Jasmine.

JOHN ꞁ A walk for peace?

JASMINE ꞁ Exactly.

JOHN ꞁ A long-necked waddle for peace?

JASMINE ꞁ Lovely.

JOHN ꞁ Can you leave these ideas with us Jasmine, because they're substantial and very interesting.

JASMINE ꞁ Yes, by all means.

JOHN ꞁ Thank you very much for coming by.

JASMINE ı Good to see you. Bye now.

Jasmine leaves the room.

MR WILSON ı Nice seeing you.

John turns to welcome the next contestant.

JOHN ı Now, Mr Wilson. We've got a problem, haven't we?

MR WILSON ı Il problemo. This is not good.

JOHN ı No, this is not good at all, Mr Wilson.

MR WILSON ı So what is the problem?

JOHN ı I'm right, aren't I, in assuming you put that athletic track in?

MR WILSON ı Yes, that's right.

JOHN ı Yes. Did you do this to specifications, Mr Wilson?

MR WILSON ı Yes.

John points to some figures.

BRYAN ı Are these the specifications, here, Mr Wilson?

Mr Wilson recognises the figures.

MR WILSON ı Yes. That's them.

BRYAN ı Good.

JOHN ı Mr Wilson, have you measured the 100-metre track?

MR WILSON ı Yes, of course.

JOHN ı Well, let me ask you, how long is it?

MR WILSON ı How long is the 100-metre track?

JOHN ı Yes.

MR WILSON ı It's a 100-metre track.

JOHN ı I know what it is, Mr Wilson. I'm asking you how long it is.

MR WILSON ı It's about 100 metres long.

JOHN ı About 100 metres long. How long should it be, Mr Wilson?

MR WILSON ı That's about the length it should be.

JOHN ı About 100 metres long.

JOHN ı Is the 200-metre track about 200 metres long?

MR WILSON ı Well, the 200-metre track is different.

BRYAN ı Isn't it twice as long as the 100 metres?

MR WILSON ı The 200-metre is different.

JOHN ı No, no, no, you've lost us.

MR WILSON ı The 200-metre track is part of the 400-metre track.

JOHN ı How long is the 400-metre track, Mr Wilson?

MR WILSON ı Well, the 400 metres starts around here in the back straight and it finishes up here at the finish line. It's a staggered start.

JOHN ı Yes, I'm familiar with the event itself, Mr Wilson. What I'm trying to ascertain is: are you absolutely sure that the 200-metre track is 200 metres long?

MR WILSON ı Yes. That's right.

JOHN ı Yes. Because it's half the 400-metre track which is 400 metres long.

MR WILSON ı That's right. The 200 metres is half the 400 metres — you can measure it.

JOHN ı No, no. But the 400-metre track is exactly 400 metres long, is it?

MR WILSON ı That's right.

JOHN ı So the 200-metre track is exactly 200 metres long.

MR WILSON ı Yes, of course.

JOHN ı But what you're telling me is the 100-metre track is *about* 100 metres long.

MR WILSON ı Slightly different arrangement, the 100-metre track.

JOHN ı Is a metre a slightly different concept in the 100 metres as against the 200?

MR WILSON ı No.

JOHN ı I don't understand then, Mr Wilson, quite why in the construction of a

100-metre track you would want to depart too radically from the constraints laid down for us by the conventional calibration of distance.

MR WILSON ı The 100-metre track is not part of the 400-metre track. It starts way out there.

JOHN ı Mr Wilson, it doesn't matter whether it's horizontal or vertical, 100 metres is 100 metres.

MR WILSON ı No two 100-metre tracks are ever the same. Everybody knows that.

JOHN ı Well, how long is *our* 100-metre track?

MR WILSON ı Look, what's your point?

JOHN ı The point, Mr Wilson, is that in 739 days we are going to hold the Olympic 100-metre final on that track. This is an event that will be watched by about 600 million of the world's most dedicated rugged individualists. You and I both know it's going to be run on a track that's *not* 100 metres long.

MR WILSON ı How do you know that?

JOHN ı Mr Wilson. Do you know who is the current 100 metres all-comers Australian record holder?

MR WILSON ı Can I guess?

JOHN ı There's not much point in guessing, Mr Wilson.

MR WILSON ı Is he an African American?

JOHN ı He's not an African American, no.

MR WILSON ı Is he that Canadian from Jamaica?

JOHN ı No, he's not a Canadian from Jamaica.

MR WILSON ı I give up.

JOHN ı The 100-metre record in this country, Mr Wilson, is currently held by Bryan.

MR WILSON ı Bryan?

BRYAN ı Yes.

Mr Wilson extends his hand.

MR WILSON ı Congratulations.

BRYAN ı Thank you.

JOHN ı A new mark, Mr Wilson, set at a blistering session last Wednesday. I wish you'd been there. We were down there and we had a bet.

MR WILSON ı Was this wind assisted?

JOHN ı No, and we'd had a couple, and in my view, Bryan is not in quite the nick he was in the same stage of last season.

Mr Wilson considers the position.

MR WILSON ı So you've measured the track?

JOHN ı Yes, we've measured the track, Mr Wilson.

MR WILSON ı So you know how long the 100-metre track is?

JOHN ı Yes, we do.

MR WILSON ı Okay.

JOHN | How long is it, Mr Wilson?

MR WILSON | You *know* how long it is.

JOHN | I want to hear you say it.

MR WILSON | Ninety-four metres.

JOHN | Ninety-four metres. Ninety-four metres. We've got a new event, haven't we, Mr Wilson?

BRYAN | The 94 metres.

JOHN | In fact we've got two new events haven't we? The 94 metres for men and the 94 metres for women.

BRYAN | Hang on. Would that replace the 100 metres or would this be a new event, because there'd be a cost element there, wouldn't there?

MR WILSON | No. That'd be in *place* of the 100 metres.

JOHN | Why?

MR WILSON | You don't have a 100-metre event. You haven't got a 100-metre track.

Media centre, Wednesday 9.34 a.m. Mr Robertson's press conference is about to start.

GINA | Fran, hi! Here's that information Robbo asked f . . . Mr Robertson asked for.

FRAN | John Clarke?

GINA | Not last time I looked. Gina Riley.

FRAN | John?

GINA | No. John not here. Brochure here. Environmental Aspects of the Staging of the Olympic Games. Everything Robbo . . . Mr Robertson needs.

FRAN | I'll put it out there for him.

Back at the office.

BRYAN | You know, we could add some metres to the 200 metres, John. Make it 206 metres. That way, anyone having a crack at the double will cover the right amount of ground.

JOHN ⏐ Yes, but after two races, you mean.

BRYAN ⏐ Yes. Amortise it over 300 metres.

JOHN ⏐ And make it compulsory to go in both.

MR WILSON ⏐ Problem solved.

Phone rings.

JOHN *(Answers phone)* ⏐ Hello, Dead Builder Proprietary Limited. Yes. Oh good. Thank you very much. *(Hangs up, turns to Mr Wilson and Bryan)* Ladies and gentlemen, Robbo has commenced. *(Picks up remote control and turns television on)* Stay there, Mr Wilson. Haven't finished with you yet.

ROBBO *(On TV)* ⏐ . . . Requiring prospective designers and builders to include an environmental tender specification when bidding for work. This specification must include all environmental aspects such as design, construction and project operation. Furthermore as part of the opening ceremony we plan to release dove-shaped balloons in three sizes. These balloons will be made from recyclable material and will disintegrate on contact with water.

At the media centre where the press conference is actually happening, things seem to be going well . . .

FRAN ⏐ Very impressive.

GINA ⏐ Cutting edge.

ROBBO ⏐ Furthermore, the tableware at the Olympic village will be made of apple fibre and potato. The plates are being made up of 25 per cent apple pulp, which is ideal for later use as solid fuel or compost.

At the office, there is some concern about this.

BRYAN ⏐ That was Nagano.

JOHN ⏐ Yes, he's got that wrong.

At the media centre, Gina freezes.

GINA ⏐ That was Nagano.

ROBBO ⏐ And central to our catering arrangements for the Games, 100,000 plates will be made out of potato starch for the serving of traditional meals such as seaweed and sushi . . .

At the office.

JOHN ⏐ That's the wrong brochure.

At the media centre.

GINA ⏐ Wrong brochure. John's really stuffed this up.

At the office.

JOHN ⏐ Gina's really stuffed this up.

At the media centre.

GINA ⏐ That was Nagano.

FRAN *(Whispers from off-stage to Robbo)* ⏐ That was Nagano.

ROBBO ⏐ . . . very much in the manner of the measures undertaken at the recent winter Olympics in Nagano.

At the office, Robbo's silken sidestep is impressive.

JOHN ⏐ He's good.

At the media centre, Gina is also impressed.

GINA ⏐ He's good.

At the office.

JOHN ⏐ He's very good.

At the media centre.

ROBBO ⏐ I have met President Samaranch and I find him a very upstanding man.

At the office.

JOHN | He's a bloody genius, this bloke. Oh well, Gina's got that in hand. *(Turns off the television. Bryan addresses Mr Wilson)*

BRYAN | How can there not have been enough land?

MR WILSON | Well, the starting area for the 100 metres isn't on the actual track itself.

JOHN | No, of course it isn't. It never has been.

MR WILSON | The 100 metres starts out here, joins the track here and finishes at the finishing line here. Now, there's a problem with enough ground at the starting area and the first part of the track. Everyone tried to fix it. No-one could. There is simply not enough land out there.

JOHN | There's a bucketload of land out there.

MR WILSON | There is *now*. But there wasn't when we started. All the cabling for the whole stadium comes in there.

BRYAN | What cabling?

MR WILSON | Television, Internet, you name it. Comes in at that corner — the masts are out there — it goes in there. There's a ton and a half of cabling under that land. They didn't get it all installed by April. We had to finish by March 15th. We couldn't wait. We couldn't use it.

BRYAN | Mr Wilson, how long was the track supposed to be in the contract?

MR WILSON | A hundred metres.

JOHN | Have you signed a completion document?

MR WILSON | Yes.

BRYAN | And who else has signed it?

MR WILSON | The Minister.

BRYAN | And does he know how long it is?

MR WILSON | No.

JOHN | How do you know that?

MR WILSON | I tried to tell him but he didn't want to know about it.

JOHN | What did he say?

MR WILSON ı He said he saw the sporting events themselves as a seamless cloth.

JOHN ı Very helpful of him.

BRYAN ı Well, he's not going to deal with it, is he?

JOHN ı See, next Wednesday Mr Wilson, we've got the New South Wales School Championships out here. Someone's going to break a world record.

MR WILSON ı Couldn't we find some way of slowing the runners down?

JOHN ı What's this 'we' stuff?

Back at Robbo's press conference, Wednesday 10.09 a.m.

REPORTER ı There are concerns that you are not living up to some of the green commitments that you've made to the IOC.

ROBBO ı You're from the ABC, aren't you?

REPORTER ı They say you've reneged on your commitment to use totally recycled water within the Olympic village.

FRAN *(From off-stage to Robbo)* ı There is a good reason for that.

ROBBO ı There is a good reason for that, and it is this:

FRAN *(Off-stage to Robbo)* ı The Hindus won't touch recycled water.

ROBBO ı The Zulus won't torch it.

REPORTER ı The Zulus won't torch it?

ROBBO ı Not in a million years. We asked them. We're not idiots.

FRAN *(Off-stage to Robbo)* ı The Indians won't drink it.

ROBBO ı West Indians want trinkets. What can I do? My hands are tied.

Fran looks at Gina in horror.

Back at the office.

MR WILSON ı We could actually dig up all the cabling and relocate and reset the 100-metre track so it's exactly 100 of your precious metres.

BRYAN ı When can we do that?

MR WILSON ꟾ But you'll lose the entire first three rows right round the entire stadium.

BRYAN ꟾ What, the whole way round?

JOHN ꟾ Consider them lost.

BRYAN ꟾ We can't do that.

JOHN ꟾ We've got to do something, Bryan. Take them out.

BRYAN ꟾ John, we can't do that. We can't afford it.

JOHN ꟾ Take them out. Take them out.

BRYAN ꟾ John, John, listen to me. We're talking about 3000 tickets times fifteen days. Think about that. Think about the revenue we're going to lose here. The media's already measuring us up for a very big necktie over the ticketing issue. On top of that I've got the IOC with their hand out for their share, the International Federation's begging for an increased allotment and I've got the Federal Government going through my rubbish bin for what's left. I was actually hoping at some stage to squeeze a member of the public through a hole in the fence, given that they partake in the rather old-fashioned pastime of actually paying for their tickets.

JOHN ⏐ I'm a humble man, Master Copperfield, but I refuse to be remembered as he who ran the 100 metres at the Sydney Olympics over 94 metres.

BRYAN ⏐ Oh, preferring to be remembered, John, as the man who left his children and grandchildren with so much public debt that they were forced to go through their lives denying themselves the small luxuries of schools and hospitals? Come on!

JOHN ⏐ The Sydney Olympics will have a 100 metres that is run over 100 metres.

BRYAN ⏐ And my grandchildren will spell.

JOHN ⏐ Bryan, if you run the 100 metres over the correct distance I'll give you a personal guarantee you're not going to lose the front three rows.

MR WILSON ⏐ No, you will lose them.

JOHN ⏐ No, no. Bear with me Mr Wilson. If I go to the final of the 100 metres and I go right down here and I sit in the front, in the front row, there's no-one sitting in front of me, I've got a completely unimpeded view of the track, what row am I sitting in?

MR WILSON ⏐ Is this the 100 metres or the 94 metres?

JOHN ⏐ This is the 100 metres, Mr Wilson.

MR WILSON ⏐ You'll be in about the fourth row.

JOHN ⏐ No, no, I'm in the front row. There's no-one in front of me.

MR WILSON ⏐ The fourth row.

JOHN ⏐ No, no, no. There must, by definition, be a front row. That's where I'm sitting. The second row's behind me. The third row's behind that, and the fourth row's behind that. Bryan, if you take out three rows they're not going to be the front three rows, they're going to be the *back* three rows.

BRYAN ⏐ John, we can't afford it. You're going to lose three rows of seats. Simple.

Back at the press conference.

REPORTER ⏐ Are you concerned that there's a perception overseas that Sydney has a pollution problem?

ROBBO ⏐ Can you believe that? Do they think that Sydney is an outer suburb of Kuala Lumpur? I hope you're all going to the Asian Games in Thailand in December. You cannot see it for smog. They're planning to have the marathon finish in the respiratory ward of Bangkok General Hospital to save on ambulances.

REPORTER ❘ The green-and-gold bell frog that is native to the Homebush area is on the endangered species list. There was talk at one stage of it being added to the list of Olympic mascots.

ROBBO ❘ No, no, Paul. I think I can say without fear of serious contradiction that the endangered green-and-gold bell frog will not be added to the ongoing list of Olympic mascots for a very simple reason.

REPORTER ❘ Why not?

ROBBO ❘ Paul, if you'd done your reading you would have noted that the green-and-gold bell frog has been removed from the official endangered species list, a fact that was announced at a ceremony last week on the shores of Homebush Bay.

REPORTER ❘ Who was there?

ROBBO ❘ Oh, everyone was there, Paul. People from the Environment Department, the Minister, Wildlife and Fisheries Department, Soil Erosion Authority and representatives of the major green organisations.

REPORTER ❘ Were the frogs there?

ROBBO ❘ No, no, the frogs weren't there, Paul. We didn't send them an invitation. We assumed, obviously erroneously, that frogs can't read.

REPORTER ❘ Robbo, the World Wildlife Fund and other green groups that were excluded from the ceremony suggested the reason the frogs weren't there is that the frogs are now extinct.

ROBBO ❘ Well, either way, they're off the endangered list.

Back at the office.

BRYAN ❘ We could run the 100 metres in a circle.

JOHN ❘ No, you can't do that.

BRYAN ❘ Yes you can. You put a circular 100 in the middle of the track out there.

JOHN ❘ You can't do that.

BRYAN ❘ Yes we can. If we can fit in a circular 400, we can fit in a circular 100.

JOHN ❘ No, you can't have a 100 with a bend in it.

BRYAN ❘ Of course you can. The 200's got a bend in it. The 400's just one dirty big bend all the way round. Why would someone object to the 100 metres having a bend in it?

JOHN ı Well, they won't run in it.

BRYAN ı Who won't?

JOHN ı The athletes. They'll refuse.

BRYAN ı Well, *I'd* run in it.

JOHN ı The best athletes won't run in it, Bryan.

BRYAN ı All the better for me. I'm the current Australian champion.

JOHN ı Try and be serious.

BRYAN ı I am being serious. There are no rules saying the 100 metres has to be run in a straight line.

JOHN ı They will get dizzy.

BRYAN ı But it's exciting. Think about this, John. The problem with the 100 metres at the moment is you know who's going to win because you know who's in front. Now, the 400 metres — you don't know who's in front until they straighten up at the top of the straight. It's fantastic. The crowd loves it.

JOHN ı If you run the 100 in a circle, Bryan, they're not going to straighten up till they get home.

BRYAN ı Wouldn't that be a ball-tearer?

JOHN ı Bryan, if the world champion draws the outside lane in your event the centrifugal force acting on him when he comes off the home turn will be absolutely enormous. He'll rip his freckle out. He'll be up over here like a bloody sheep dog across the top of the crowd. We'll be going to guarantee the safety of the public.

BRYAN ı It would be a ball-tearer, though.

JOHN ı It'd be a bloody sight worse than that, Bryan.

They consider their options for a moment.

JOHN ı Perhaps we shouldn't be thinking about these things solely in terms of distance. These aren't questions of distance, are they? They're questions of time.

BRYAN ı What are?

JOHN ı Athletics. I mean, races are not really a question of distance. They're a question of time.

BRYAN ı No, they're not.

JOHN ı Yes, they are. How long is a marathon?

BRYAN ı It's a set distance.

MR WILSON ı Twenty-six miles and something.

JOHN ı Yes. Are they all flat?

BRYAN ı No, there are hills.

JOHN ı Where are the hills in the Amsterdam marathon?

MR WILSON ı There aren't hills in all of them.

JOHN ı So they're *not* all the same. There's the 26 miles with the hills and the 26 miles without hills.

MR WILSON ı It's the same distance.

BRYAN ı It's a very long race, John.

JOHN ı Oh yes, the one with the hills is a hell of a thing, Bryan.

MR WILSON ı What about the 1500 metres?

BRYAN ı Yes, the 1500 metres race is the same all over the world.

JOHN ı Completely different. Completely different.

BRYAN ı How is it different?

MR WILSON ı Surely a metre is a metre anywhere in the world?

JOHN ı I beg your pardon?

MR WILSON ı A metre is an internationally agreed standard unit of measure.

JOHN ı Listen pal, you'd want to be on my side on this, wouldn't you? I'm trying to dig you out of a very deep bear-pit.

MR WILSON ı I appreciate that.

JOHN ı Lift your game, son. We're going to get cleaned up by the Australian sprint champion here if you're not careful.

MR WILSON ı So what's your point?

JOHN ı Have you ever been in a 1500-metre race?

MR WILSON ǀ No.

JOHN ǀ Why do you think the runners like running along the inside lane?

MR WILSON ǀ So they don't have to run as far.

JOHN ǀ That's my boy. I thought I'd lost you for a moment there.

MR WILSON ǀ That's not the point here though, is it?

JOHN ǀ In the 94 metres? No, the 94's a straight event. You just run it in your lane. *(A ghastly thought occurs to John)* You did put the lanes in, didn't you?

MR WILSON ǀ Of course I did.

Back at the press conference, Wednesday 10.32 a.m.

FEMALE REPORTER ǀ Mr Robertson?

ROBBO ǀ Yes, sweetheart?

FEMALE REPORTER ǀ While a woman heads the organising committee for Athens 2004, there are only a handful involved in the Sydney organising committee.

ROBBO ǀ You have authority for that proposition do you, darling?

FEMALE REPORTER ǀ How did they come to be breached in the first place, Robbo?

ROBBO ǀ How did what come to be breached, Nicole?

FEMALE REPORTER ǀ The guidelines.

ROBBO ǀ According to whom, Nicole?

FEMALE REPORTER ǀ Greenpeace.

ROBBO ǀ Oh Greenpeace. Yes, well. All right, let's get Greenpeace to organise the Games, shall we? We'll all snuggle up and watch the 4 × 100 bottle recycling. Now, let's get this straight once and for all. Hands up all those who at some stage of their life have been the Federal Minister for the Environment. *(He looks around)* Oh, just me? Let me tell you something then. For three years I had to climb into a kaftan once a fortnight and belt out a few verses of the old 'Kumbaya'. You know why?

FEMALE REPORTER ǀ Because of your commitment to the environment, Robbo?

ROBBO ǀ I had to stop at every third mud-brick hut in the jungle and glad hand every dead-beat who poked a stick of incense in my direction, so you can believe me when

I tell you that I am more than well and truly qualified to ignore *everything* that Greenpeace has to say about anything.

FEMALE REPORTER ⏐ You've still breached the guidelines.

ROBBO ⏐ I'm glad you've got such a high opinion of me, Nicole, but I'm not responsible for everything that happens in the preparation of these Games. Nor can I do everything. Kevin Nowra of my office is in charge of the day-to-day operations at Homebush.

FEMALE REPORTER ⏐ There's talk that his position is under review.

Fran makes a call on her mobile phone.

ROBBO ⏐ Look, I'll make this clear enough, even for you, Nicole. Kevin Nowra has my complete support.

Back at the office.

BRYAN ⏐ That's it for Kevin then.

JOHN ⏐ Yes. Say goodnight to the folks, Kevin.

MR WILSON ⏐ He'll be right. He's got Robbo's complete support.

JOHN ⏐ Having Robbo's full support is often the last sound people hear. They just hear they have Robbo's full confidence and a nice man pops a bag over their head.

Back at the press conference . . .

FRAN *(On mobile phone)* ⏐ Hold on, hold on a minute. *(To Gina)* What did he say?

GINA ⏐ He said Kevin Nowra has his complete support.

FRAN *(On mobile phone)* ⏐ Forget that. Call Nowra and get his carpark pass. He's gone apparently.

At the office.

ROBBO *(On telly)* ⏐ And we took that background into the ALP.

John turns off the television.

BRYAN ı We'll have to talk to the media.

JOHN ı Well, only if they find out something about this.

MR WILSON ı They don't know anything at the moment.

JOHN ı Did you register a formal complaint about not being able to use that land?

MR WILSON ı No. We were just told to start there. *(Gestures)*

JOHN ı It might be worth getting something in writing about that.

MR WILSON ı Well, what's the point? The thing's bloody built.

BRYAN ı It's always a good idea to get something in writing though.

JOHN ı Perhaps not a formal complaint, just something that registers that it's not our fault.

MR WILSON ı It's not my fault either.

JOHN ı Oh no.

MR WILSON ı We need to talk to someone at broadcasting. There's a minister, isn't there?

BRYAN ı Yes, but we need to speak to the person who actually runs it.

JOHN ı No question about that. We'd want to go to the top.

BRYAN ı Robbo.

JOHN ı Yes, I'll talk to Robbo. *(Extension buzzes)* No calls, thank you.

RECEPTIONIST ı Robert Walkley on the phone.

JOHN ı Robert Walkley? Robert Walkley? Panel?

BRYAN ı Writes for the *Star*.

JOHN ı *Star*?

BRYAN ı Weekly tabloid. Light-hearted mixture of racism and pornography.

RECEPTIONIST ı He says it's important.

JOHN ı Tell him to take a number.

RECEPTIONIST ı He says it's to do with the measuring of the 100 metres.

JOHN ¦ Tell him I'll ring him back when I get time. *(Pushes a button on the phone)*
Am I doing the right thing here, Bryan?

ROBERT WALKLEY ¦ Hello.

JOHN ¦ Hello.

WALKLEY ¦ Hello.

JOHN ¦ Hello. Who's that?

WALKLEY ¦ Robert Walkley, the *Post*.

JOHN ¦ Oh Robert! Nice to hear from you. How are you?

WALKLEY ¦ Am I on the speaker phone?

MR WILSON ¦ No.

BRYAN ¦ No.

WALKLEY ¦ What?

JOHN ¦ No.

WALKLEY ¦ Doesn't matter. Listen, John, it's about the 100-metre track.

JOHN ¦ Yes. What about it in particular, Robert?

WALKLEY ¦ Well there's a strong story going around that it's not the full 100 metres.

JOHN ¦ Oh well . . .

WALKLEY ¦ The second part of the story, mate, has it that the man with sole
responsibility for the measuring of the track was Kevin Nowra from Robbo's office.
Do you have any comment to make?

JOHN ¦ Robert, I'm obviously extremely limited in what I can say on this subject at
this particular time and I'll say to you only what I've said to our people and I speak for
everyone here on this issue, and you can quote me on this Robert — Kevin Nowra has
our complete support.

PAST SPORTS STARS AND GENDER

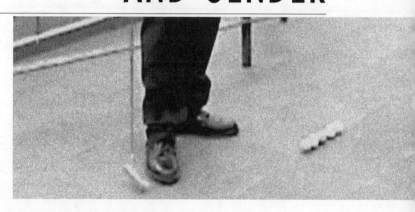

John walks into the office clasping a wad of newspaper clippings.

JOHN ı Good morning. Bit crisp this morning, isn't it?

BRYAN *(On phone)* ı Come off it, Craig. Vladimir Kuts? Not in the same class.

The phone rings in John's office. Gina answers.

GINA ı Olympic Hotline, Gina speaking. Thank you. Thank you. That's beautiful singing. Thank you. Thank you.

JOHN ı Good morning.

GINA ı Good morning.

JOHN ı What are you doing in here?

GINA ı Kevin from Marketing just rang to wish me happy birthday.

JOHN ı Oh, happy birthday.

GINA ı Thank you.

JOHN ı I didn't know you knew anyone in Marketing.

GINA ı Never met or spoken with Kevin in my born days. He's obviously done one of those marketing courses that tells you to find out the birthday of everyone in your organisation, pop it in your diary and give them a call on the big day, no doubt in order to prove what a particularly genuine type of person you are. *(She is dialling as she speaks)*

JOHN ı Where's my stapler?

GINA ı Kevin in Marketing, please. Oh Kevin, it's Gina. *(He doesn't recognise her name)* Gina. Never mind. Listen, I just rang to wish you a happy birthday. It's not? Well, it's in my diary. Let me check. I see . . . Oh, it's Brad Pitt's birthday. I see the confusion. He's someone else I've never met and couldn't give a shit about. And Kevin, one more thing . . . *(Slams down phone)*

John is still looking for his stapler and wanders down the corridor and into Bryan's office.

JOHN ı Stapler? Stapler?

BRYAN *(Still on phone)* ı This is the Russian Vladimir Kuts we're talking about here, Craig is it? Come off it. Cathy Freeman with a wooden leg would have beaten Vladimir Kuts. If he went any bloody slower he would have been going backwards.

JOHN ı Stapler?

BRYAN *(On phone)* ı Hang on a second, Craig.

JOHN ı Stapler? Stapler?

BRYAN ı Yes. What are you . . . ?

JOHN ı Have we got a stapler, Bryan? We must have a stapler. We're the Olympics. We must run to a stapler. *(Leaves Bryan's office for Gina's)* Ah! Something that looks a bit like a stapler.

As he enters Gina's office he hears the radio. As is the case every morning, community concerns are articulated through discourse with Albert Einstein, a radio talkback host. John is fortunate to experience the following.

CALLER ı Morning Alby.

EINSTEIN ı Morning.

CALLER | Alby, I'm opposed to the new freeway plan because it involves the demolition of my house.

EINSTEIN | Hang . . . hang on . . . It involves what?

CALLER | The demolition of my house.

EINSTEIN | Yes, what about it?

CALLER | The freeway plan involves the demolition of my house.

EINSTEIN | Hang on, hang on. What involves the demolition of your house?

CALLER | The freeway plan.

EINSTEIN | Yes, what's all this got to do with your house?

CALLER | It involves the demolition of my house.

EINSTEIN | Hang . . . hang on. What does?

CALLER | The freeway plan.

EINSTEIN | What are you talking about?

CALLER | The freeway plan involves the demolition of my house.

EINSTEIN | What you're saying is that the freeway plan involves the demolition of your house.

CALLER | Yes.

EINSTEIN | Is that what you're saying?

CALLER | Yes.

EINSTEIN | That it involves the demolition of your house?

CALLER | Yes.

EINSTEIN | The actual demolition.

CALLER | Yes.

EINSTEIN | Of your entire house.

CALLER | Yes.

EINSTEIN | The house you live in.

CALLER | Yes.

EINSTEIN ı Won't be there any more.

CALLER ı No.

EINSTEIN ı Gone.

CALLER ı Yes.

EINSTEIN ı Why?

CALLER ı Because of the freeway plan.

John is impressed.

JOHN ı Whatever they pay that bloke, it's simply not enough.

Gina is looking through binoculars in John's office. She looks out at the arena, which is not yet completed.

GINA ı This stadium's never going to be finished at this rate.

JOHN ı Any sign of my stapler out there?

GINA ı There's a labourer over there in about Section 12. He has not so much as farted in twenty minutes. Look at him.

BRYAN *(Walking into the office)* ı Vladimir Kuts. What an idiot!

JOHN ı Vladimir Kuts is an idiot?

BRYAN ı No. No. No. Craig.

JOHN ı Craig? Who might Craig be?

BRYAN ı Craig from Accounts Receivable. Going on with the same old crap about how the athletes of the past are better than the athletes today.

JOHN ı Have you seen my stapler? Blue stapler.

BRYAN ı No. I told you I haven't seen it.

JOHN ı It must exist somewhere. Craig might be a bit of a bore, Bryan, but I'll tell you something for nothing — on that issue he is absolutely right.

BRYAN ı Oh not you too, John. Come on, your modern athlete is a machine.

JOHN ı That may be, Bryan, but your older athletes used to root, shoot, drive a truck, work sixteen hours a day, yank a pair of shorts on, try and get a bit of training in at lunchtime.

Your modern athlete . . . Incidentally we have to go to the IOC about this GST thing. *(Points to phone)* How do you work that? *(Presses a button and speaks to receptionist)* Could you give us a whistle the minute this GST package arrives, please.

BRYAN ı And your point is?

JOHN ı Your modern athlete, Bryan, lives in a thermostatically controlled biosphere for eleven months of the year wrapped in mung beans or something and they're still only 10 per cent faster.

BRYAN ı Oh rubbish.

JOHN ı They are. Go and look it up. Do a bit of compare and contrast.

BRYAN ı I will. It's a lot of rubbish.

JOHN ı Blue stapler. Look for that too.

BRYAN ı Rubbish.

John approaches Gina.

JOHN ı Gina, that bloke might move if you stop watching him. A watched pot never boils.

GINA ı You're blinding me with science. Some respect, please. I'm on phone duty.

JOHN ı We're all on phone duty.

GINA ı No, I'm on special phone duty.

JOHN ı Special phone duty? What's special phone duty?

GINA ı Upstairs thought it might be a good idea to establish a freecall Olympic hotline so that intending overseas visitors could call with their queries about our beautiful city.

JOHN ı That's actually not a bad idea.

GINA ı It's a shocking idea, John. The line is only open from 9 till 5.

JOHN ı You can't have people working 24 hours a day.

GINA ı Having a phone line that operates only in Australian business hours is not much good for the rest of the world, is it?

JOHN ı Well, it's probably not bad for Asia or something.

GINA ı Asia's broke, John. They called this morning to say they're not coming.

John is still looking for his stapler. He has a handful of loose papers.
He looks behind the couch and is pleased to have found something.

JOHN ı Lord Lucan, how are you? Have you got my stapler? *(He comes back to Gina)* I thought we had an auditorium full of people doing this.

GINA ı No.

JOHN ı We did. I saw them. It was like *Gandhi* with phones.

GINA ı We did until yesterday, yes, when the Federal and State Governments couldn't agree which one of them was going to pay for it.

JOHN ı What do they want to know? How is it going?

GINA ı What do they want to know? Most of them want to know if the Games are still on.

JOHN ı Of course the Games are still on.

GINA ı Foreign newspapers have been full of stories about the collapse of the Asian economies. Most callers think we can't afford to hold the Games and we're going to cancel them.

JOHN ı Why would anybody think we're part of Asia?

GINA ı Because we spent the best part of ten years telling them we are.

JOHN ı Well I don't think . . .

Bryan walks in with a reference book.

BRYAN ı Here you go: your average marathon runner is 22 per cent faster than he was 50 years ago.

JOHN ı He's fitter. I didn't say he wasn't fitter.

BRYAN ı John, you are a broken record.

JOHN ı Bryan, he'd want to be a bit faster wouldn't he? In 1924 at the Paris Olympics, at the start of the marathon, the runners were only crouched down because they were stubbing out cigars.

BRYAN ı Oh, come on.

JOHN | You've got to make some introductory remarks, incidentally, about a GST.

Jonathan walks in with a newspaper for Gina.

GINA | Thank you, Jonathan.

JONATHON | The courier's on his way.

JOHN | Oh good.

BRYAN | Yes. I know about the remarks. I'll do it.

JOHN *(Points to Jonathan)* | Who's that?

Phone rings.

GINA | Olympic Hotline. Gina speaking. Just hold on a minute please.

GINA | Could you get me a biscuit please, John? And a cuppa?

JOHN | Yes, for madam. Coffee. Of course.

GINA *(Into phone)* | Yes. Certainly. No, we're not part of Asia. No, I assure you we're not.

Bryan encounters John in the gents' toilets. Bryan continues with his argument.

BRYAN | Tennis. Tennis.

JOHN | I beg your pardon?

BRYAN | Tell me tennis used to be better than it is now.

JOHN | Tennis? That's exactly what I'll tell you, Bryan.

BRYAN | You have got to be joking.

JOHN | Used to be miles better, Bryan. Tennis: a game that used to be played on an ant bed with a racquet the size of a postage stamp and a ball you had to go and get out of the neighbour's guttering. An era, Bryan, in which it was considered nobler and better to win the Davis Cup for your country than it was to win Wimbledon for yourself. It was played by players who spoke to the umpire only in the event that they wished to inquire after the state of his wife's health.

BRYAN | John, don't take it personally.

JOHN ı Bryan, the last sixteen at Wimbledon used to all come from Queensland. Every single one of them. And possibly someone from New South Wales.

BRYAN ı Absolute nonsense.

JOHN ı And they played in whites, Bryan.

BRYAN ı Oh big deal!

JOHN ı In sharp contrast, your modern tennis player, Bryan, is going to phone in sick if he has a sprained eyelash so he can stay in the sauna longer playing tonsil hockey with the supermodel *du jour*.

BRYAN ı Get a life!

JOHN ı They played in whites, Bryan. You watched them. You didn't have to read them.

BRYAN ı So what? You're mad. You're absolutely mad.

JOHN *(To camera as he leaves)* ı Let the minutes show that at this point Mr Clarke left the meeting of the Australian Rationalists' Society looking tense but dignified.

Bryan is engaged in important government work and does not realise John has gone.

BRYAN ı Give us an other example. Go on. You haven't got one, have you? See. John? John?

Back in John's office, Gina is still on the phone. John is on the couch.

GINA ı . . . But I think we all agree now that was a mistake. What more can I say? The Games are still on. No wucking furries.

Bryan walks in. He has another point to make to John.

BRYAN ı Football.

JOHN ı Hello, Bryan.

BRYAN ı Football.

JOHN ı Football.

BRYAN ı Football.

JOHN ǀ You keep saying 'football'. I presume this is a pathetic attempt to regenerate an argument in which you are being roundly thrashed.

BRYAN ǀ Oh rubbish, come on. Football.

JOHN ǀ El Niño, Bryan, has presented players of the modern era with the hardest surfaces in history. Most players under the age of twenty have never, for example, played in rain.

BRYAN ǀ You have not given me one single example in any sport where a player of today and a player of your golden past has contested under the same conditions over exactly the same course. *(Brandishes a stapler)*

JOHN ǀ Bryan . . . hey, that's my stapler!

BRYAN ǀ I'll give you this back when you give me one single example.

JOHN ǀ Bryan, I presume all this rhetoric is a clear indication you've finished your beautifully crafted first paragraph on the subject of the influence of the GST on the Olympics that you're going to talk to the IOC about?

BRYAN ǀ I have.

JOHN ǀ Give us my stapler now.

BRYAN ǀ One example.

JOHN ǀ Give us my stapler.

BRYAN ǀ One example.

JOHN ǀ Give us my stapler back now, Bryan.

BRYAN ǀ One example.

Gina is on the binoculars again.

GINA ǀ Oh, he's getting up . . . He's getting up. He's going to do some work. No, just scratching the builder's inch. No, don't do any work. That's right. Sit back down. Good on you.

Wednesday 10.24 a.m. John is in Gina's office. He's talking on the phone.

JOHN ǀ Ah Dino! It's John. Good thanks. How are you? Listen, a bit of help. Long-distance swimmer. Australian. Big bloke, 48-calibre chest. Fair-sized roof over the tool shed. Used to do the English Channel a fair bit, in about . . . yes, that's him. You're a genius. Thank you. Bye. Bryan?

Outside, Bryan is on the rooftop practising his putting.

BRYAN ၊ Beautiful. *(To John)* Not you again.

JOHN ၊ Hello, Bryan. English Channel. Des Renford.

BRYAN ၊ Des Renford?

JOHN ၊ Des Renford.

BRYAN ၊ Dessie Renford.

JOHN ၊ Des Renford would regularly take on the English Channel, Bryan. He would drop his tweeds, pull on a pair of oversized budgie smugglers and he would drop a bomb off the white cliffs of Dover and start rolling his arm over.

BRYAN ၊ Des Renford?

JOHN ၊ Yes. He would then disappear off the world's radar screens for about three weeks. Subsequently he would be found, lying on a beach near Calais somewhere, with a school of herring up his snorer. He'd be in intensive care for about a fortnight. He would then swim back to England, Bryan, and get his towel.

BRYAN ı And your point is, Mr Clarke?

JOHN ı As distinct from your modern athlete, who is provided with a waterproof five-star hotel suite which they drag from one side of the Channel to the other. It only takes about 40 minutes. They give them a wake-up call five minutes out.

BRYAN ı You're mad.

JOHN *(He gives an imaginary channel-swimmer a wake-up call)* ı Hoi! Nearly there.

BRYAN ı That's it? That's your best shot?

JOHN ı Name me your modern-day Des Renford.
          (Bryan doesn't. John opens to the contest to the broader public, driving past along the road) Anybody?

Back in the office, Gina is fielding yet another call.

GINA ı All right sir, we are Pacific-rimmers. The fact that you've never heard of a Pacific-rimmer is hardly my concern, is it? I don't give a flying f . . . *(Caller hangs up. Gina turns to camera)* What's the reverse of PR?

Wednesday 12.10 p.m. John and Bryan are in Bryan's office.

JOHN ı It's not the athletes I blame actually, Bryan. I don't blame the athletes for the fact that when I'm stuck in the traffic I've got to look up at a billboard advertising an athletic shoe that tells me there's no second prize.

BRYAN ı John, it's inspirational.

JOHN ı It must be enormously inspirational to the people who make the actual shoes, stuck in a sauna somewhere up in Asia getting about five cents a year. What are you doing?

BRYAN ı Looking for your 'off' switch.

JOHN ı It must be very inspirational to the woman on the production line, Bryan, trying to work out whether her one remaining lung allows her sufficient aerobic capacity to rugby-tackle a rat at some stage of the day so she can lug it home and feed her family.

BRYAN ⏐ John, you do not get on the cover of *Sports Illustrated* if you are the runner-up.

JOHN ⏐ That's another part of the same problem, of course. In the old days a sports magazine used to have a sportsperson on the front. Betty Cuthbert hurdling — a bit of Betty, a bit of hurdle. Nowadays you've got a supermodel on the front, in the nude, smoking a bloody cigar. There might be a synergistic relationship between Linda Evangelista's lower alimentary canal and sport of some kind, Bryan, but it bloody eludes me.

> *(Bryan hands him his stapler)* Thank you very much. Well done.

BRYAN ⏐ Fifteen–love.

COURIER *(Calling out)* ⏐ Delivery.

JOHN ⏐ Oh good. Bloody marvellous. About time too. We've got to get down to the IOC, Bryan. We've got to do this very quickly. The GST stuff will all be in here and if they ask us anything more complicated than our names we're going to be in some kind of trouble, I think.

BRYAN ⏐ Is this the GST stuff?

COURIER ⏐ Capricciosa, I think.

JOHN ⏐ This is a pizza?

COURIER ⏐ Yes, pizza.

GINA *(From inside John's office)* ⏐ For the birthday girl!

JOHN *(Takes pizza into office for Gina)* ⏐ Oh, I am terribly sorry. That is much more important, isn't it, than the impact of the GST and the ensuing tax package on the entire Olympics.

GINA ⏐ I only ordered that ten minutes ago. Geez, they're good, this new mob. Thank you.

BRYAN ⏐ Have you got everything you need?

GINA *(She is in binocularworld again)* ⏐ They do not want to work, these people. Look at them. Yes, that's right. Sit down. Good on you.

John's mobile phone rings.

JOHN ⏐ Hello. Yes it is. Oh yes, really. Where? Yes, oh I see. *(He looks out the window across the arena and waves his hand)* Which window am I doing something in?

Very good. Okay. *(To Gina)* Gina, this is the concreters in — *(On phone)* where did you say? — B15? Yes, B15.

GINA ı Hello.

JOHN *(To Gina)* ı Yes. They've got a couple of questions they want to ask you. *(On phone)* Fire away. *(To Gina)* Are you a statue? *(To Gina)* What are you being paid? *(To Bryan)* What are funbags, Bryan? *(On phone)* Yes, and the rest of the afternoon to you too, Jack. *(To Bryan)* Have a bit of pizza, Bryan.

BRYAN ı Oh, thank you. *(He tries to take a piece but it proves difficult to pick up)*

JOHN ı Get into it. No grab it. You've got to grab it firmly, boy. Grab it firmly. There's a good boy.

BRYAN ı It won't come up.

JOHN ı Not from a very big family are you, Bryan? Oh, I'm terribly sorry — did you want a piece of pizza that isn't stapled to the bottom?

BRYAN ı Hilarious, isn't he?

Gina's phone rings.

GINA ı Hello. Welcome to the island continent.

Bryan Dawe visits the Minister's Secretary to discuss the seating arrangements for a regional delegates meeting.

BRYAN *(To camera)* ı You guys will have to stay here, I'm afraid. I'll have to check this out. He's expecting the three of us, all right?

In Nicholas Bell's office, Bryan sits and they have the plan spread out before them.

BRYAN ı So who's going from here?

NICHOLAS ı There is you, Gina, Don Talbot, Ric Charlesworth, Tracey Holmes. *(He crosses out one of those names)* They're sending through a final seating arrangement this afternoon.

BRYAN ı Isn't this the seating here?

NICHOLAS ǀ No, it's been changed. We're sitting here at the European table in this plan but we have been shifted.

BRYAN ǀ Why were we at the European table?

NICHOLAS ǀ I think they meant culturally.

BRYAN ǀ We've got nothing to do with Europe.

NICHOLAS ǀ That's what the Belgians and the Portuguese said.

BRYAN ǀ So where are we?

NICHOLAS ǀ We've been invited to sit here at the Scandinavian table.

BRYAN ǀ They're hardly synonymous, are they? Australia and Scandinavia?

NICHOLAS (*Explaining the connection*) ǀ There's room at the Scandinavian table.

BRYAN ǀ What about Oceania? New Zealand? Solomon Islands? Fiji?

NICHOLAS ǀ No. We have been vetoed.

BRYAN ǀ Guam?

NICHOLAS | Apparently Australian mining companies are causing too much trouble in Nauru and Papua New Guinea. *(Nicholas's mobile phone rings)* Excuse me again. *(On phone)* Hello. Hello. God, these things are bloody useless. *(Bryan presses a button on his phone)*

BRYAN | Completely useless.

NICHOLAS | Apparently you're supposed to get reception in 97 per cent of the country.

BRYAN | It must be the other 97 per cent.

NICHOLAS *(Back to the seating plan)* | Look, we could just sit at 'Other'.

BRYAN | We can't be 'Other'. We're the bloody host.

NICHOLAS | All right. It has been suggested that we invent another table.

BRYAN | Called what?

NICHOLAS | 'Host Cities'. We invent another table called 'Host Cities' and invite the last two and the next two as well.

BRYAN | And who would that be?

NICHOLAS | Well, there'd be someone from Athens, someone from Nagano.

BRYAN | And someone from Coca-Cola and a Mormon.

NICHOLAS | That'd be right. *(Nicholas's mobile phone rings again)* Excuse me, sorry. Hello? *(To Bryan)* Why don't they stop ringing until they get to an area where I can talk to them? *(To phone)* Hello?

BRYAN | They drive you mad, those things.

NICHOLAS | Hello? No, look. It's even got the number of the person to talk to and I can't talk to him.

BRYAN *(Presses a button on his phone)* | Completely useless, all of them.

NICHOLAS | Height of efficiency.

BRYAN *(Back to the seating plan)* | I don't know. How about Cuba?

NICHOLAS | Cuba's over here. Caribbean.

BRYAN | We could sit there.

NICHOLAS | They're actually very nice people.

David Pigot from the Sports Accreditation Board is on his way to John's office. He encounters the documentary-makers as he enters the lift.

DAVID *(To camera)* । You're the doco people.

REPORTER । Are you going up to the Games office?

DAVID *(To camera)* । I am. I am. Yes. I saw this on the television on Monday night. I didn't see you, I saw . . . Second floor right? Yes, I was supposed to come for a meeting on Thursday but they cancelled. Then I was supposed to come on Friday but they were interstate. I wanted to come yesterday and they were too busy. Too busy. I've got better things to do. *(Lift doors open and David gets out)* Anyway, see you later.

       (Cut to John's office, where David seems irritated) Have you seen this?

JOHN । Yes, I have. Who is Consuela?

DAVID । Carlos Sabatini. Same person.

JOHN । I realise that. I'm asking who she is.

DAVID । It's in the letter.

JOHN । David, the letter explains the problem. I want to know how it happened.

GINA । Carlos won the gold medal in skeet-shooting at Atlanta.

JOHN । Ah yes. Not an event I follow.

DAVID । He wants to come here and defend his Olympic title.

JOHN । Fair enough.

GINA । Has won the last three national championships in Argentina.

JOHN । A commendable performance.

GINA । Is current South American champion, European champion and world champion.

JOHN । Have we got to the problem yet?

DAVID । He can't come.

JOHN । Can't come to Sydney?

DAVID । No.

JOHN । Why not?

DAVID ı Not eligible to enter the event.

JOHN ı Any reason given, David?

DAVID ı Read the letter.

JOHN ı I'm asking you.

DAVID ı Not eligible. Can't go in it. Doesn't qualify.

GINA ı In February 1998 at the El Hambro Clinic in Buenos Aires, Carlos had a sex-change operation.

JOHN ı I see.

DAVID ı And he's now a woman.

JOHN ı This is Consuela?

DAVID ı That's exactly right. Yes.

JOHN ı And who says Consuela can't come?

DAVID ı The Olympic Sports Accreditation Board. We control who is allowed to come and who isn't.

JOHN ı And you've decided Consuela's not coming.

DAVID ı That's exactly right.

JOHN ı What are the issues here?

DAVID ı There aren't any issues here. He's not coming.

A slight pause occurs.

JOHN ı He's the defending champion.

DAVID ı He's a woman.

JOHN ı Let him compete in the women's event.

DAVID ı He's the men's world champion.

GINA ı He was a woman when he won it.

DAVID ı Yes, but that wasn't known at the time.

JOHN ı Somebody must have known.

DAVID ┃ Nobody knew.

JOHN ┃ Did Carlos have any kind of inkling?

DAVID ┃ Well, no-one else knew.

JOHN ┃ All the other competitors were men, were they?

DAVID ┃ Of course they were.

JOHN ┃ Although, of course, you couldn't possibly have known that at the time.

DAVID ┃ No, we knew that the rest of them were men at the time.

JOHN ┃ At the time, David, you must have thought they were all men.

DAVID ┃ How the hell could we have known who was a woman and who was a man?

JOHN ┃ My point is, how the hell can you know that about anybody?

DAVID ┃ Oh don't be bloody stupid. You can tell.

JOHN ┃ David, if you could tell a man from a woman, how did a woman win the men's world championship?

GINA ┃ Look, this is a disaster. 'We call upon the athletes of the world to come and compete in Sydney regardless of colour, race or creed. So long as you fit the gender requirements'.

Another slight pause occurs.

JOHN ┃ What do the other shooters think?

GINA ┃ The other shooters don't have a problem.

JOHN ┃ David, Sabotini is the defending champion, isn't she?

DAVID ┃ No.

GINA ┃ Yes, she is.

DAVID ┃ No, he isn't. You can only be the defending champion if you're defending your title.

JOHN ┃ But the only reason she's not doing that is that you're not going to let her in.

DAVID ┃ Well, you can't be the defending champion if you're not defending your title. Can you?

GINA ⏐ Look, what is the difference between men's skeet shooting and women's skeet shooting aside from gender?

DAVID ⏐ What do you mean 'aside from gender'? Gender is the difference.

JOHN ⏐ Are the skeets the same? Are the targets the same? Is the gear the same? Are the rifles the same? Is the scoring system the same?

DAVID ⏐ Yes, yes, yes, yes, yes.

GINA ⏐ Why have they got separate events?

DAVID ⏐ Well, all sports have separate events. You have a men's 100 metres and you have a women's 100 metres. Are you going to have them run together?

GINA ⏐ Yes, but this is not an event that involves strength or speed. Gender is just an idea that's been imposed on them.

DAVID ⏐ No, it isn't.

GINA ⏐ It's a social construct.

DAVID ⏐ Ridiculous. This is an Olympic event we're talking about. You can't have men and women in the same event. You don't have women rowers competing against the men. You don't have women swimmers competing against the men. You don't have women weight-lifters competing against the men.

GINA ⏐ Those are events involving physical strength.

JOHN ⏐ Yes, there's a clear difference there, David.

DAVID ⏐ Oh, so there is a difference. It's not just a social construct.

GINA ⏐ Yes, there is a difference between men and women, David. There's a difference between black and white, short and tall, bright and very, very thick.

A third slight pause occurs.

JOHN ⏐ You see, David, I think Gina's point is that it's not necessary to break everything people do up into two classes. In the case of the skeet, for example, which seems to involve aim, steadiness and experience, we might be able to make the problem go away if we can make the difference between the two groups go away.

DAVID ⏐ And my point is that you can't.

GINA ⏐ What about events where men and women compete now?

DAVID | What events?

GINA | Equestrian. A sport in which Australia is defending its four-day event gold medal in Sydney.

DAVID | Not a proper sport.

JOHN | Not a proper sport, David?

DAVID | This is different. How can this woman defend a men's title? He's a woman.

GINA | This is hopeless.

JOHN | David, she won it at the last Olympics.

DAVID | She won the men's event.

GINA | Yes, well, why can't she defend it?

DAVID | Only a man can defend a men's title.

GINA | Name a single man on earth who can defend this title.

DAVID | I don't care about that. The ruling is very clear on that point.

GINA | No-one can defend this title!

DAVID | He should have thought about that earlier.

GINA | She might have had a few other things on her mind.

DAVID | Well, if you're not going to concentrate at this level you're going to pay the price.

Gina leaves the room. The resulting silence is broken by John.

JOHN | David, what is your definition of the problem?

DAVID | The problem is that we have two genders and we have two events.

JOHN | Can this person compete or not?

DAVID | In which event?

JOHN | In either event.

DAVID | Let's take them one at a time, shall we?

JOHN | The men's?

DAVID ⏐ No.

JOHN ⏐ The women's?

DAVID ⏐ No.

RECEPTIONIST ⏐ Call for you, John.

JOHN ⏐ That pretty much exhausts the possibilities as I see it. *(Picks up the phone)* Just excuse me for a minute will you please? Hello.

GINA ⏐ John.

JOHN ⏐ Oh, hello. *(She is in her office and we can see her but David cannot)*

GINA ⏐ Don't look over here. Look out the window and say exactly what I tell you to say. Say 'put him through'.

JOHN ⏐ Sure. Put him through.

GINA ⏐ Hello. It's Richo here.

JOHN ⏐ Richo! Yes. Yes. David's here now. We're just talking our way through it.
   Oh well, you know, there are some difficulties. It's obviously hard to put her in the men's event. She is a woman.
   Well, they don't want a man in the women's event. They're not going to let her come in and do it.

GINA ⏐ Ask Chuckles if other women are allowed to compete in the women's event.

JOHN ⏐ Just a minute, I'll ask. *(To David)* David, are other women allowed to compete in women's events?

DAVID ⏐ Yes.

JOHN *(Back to the phone)* ⏐ Yes they are.

GINA ⏐ Yes, and ask him if they can't compete in women's events, where the hell are they supposed to compete?

JOHN ⏐ I'll just check that with him. *(To David)* David, if women are not allowed to compete in the women's events, where are they supposed to compete?

DAVID ⏐ What's his point?

JOHN *(To the phone)* ⏐ Richo, David's not quite sure where you're going with this very interesting line of questioning.

GINA ⏐ That's because he's stupid.

JOHN ⏐ Yes. Hang on a minute. *(To David)* David, do you want the shooting to be a very big success at the Sydney Olympics or are you completely insane? Richo says you can only pick one.

GINA ⏐ Oh, that's beautiful, John.

JOHN ⏐ He's having a bit of a think about that one, Richo.

Oh, I think he would see that Friday is an excellent opportunity to make an announcement to the world press in fact, that the current world men's skeet champion will be competing in the women's event at the Sydney Olympics. One thing, Richo, when David goes to make this announcement, could he take Gina with him?

GINA ⏐ No!

JOHN ⏐ Oh good, he can.

GINA ⏐ John!

JOHN ⏐ Fantastic. That'd be great.

GINA ⏐ John! I don't want to go with him. He's a little prick.

JOHN ⏐ Thank you. I'll tell him. Bye. *(To David)* That was Richo, David. Do you want a cup of tea?

John walks out of his office and meets Gina in the corridor.

GINA ⏐ How did that go?

JOHN ⏐ That seemed to go fairly well, thank you.

GINA ⏐ Why did you make him take me with him on Friday?

JOHN ⏐ Well, you'd want to hear the words coming out of his mouth, wouldn't you? *(To camera)* And you can cut this bit out. You'd want to hear him actually say it. Would you trust him? *(To camera)* Cut it bloody out.

Bryan comes back into the office.

BRYAN ⏐ Morning.

JOHN ⏐ Oh, good morning. Good morning.

GINA ⏐ How did you go?

BRYAN ⏐ Fair to average. The regional delegates thing is a complete shambles.

JOHN ı Get away.

BRYAN ı The highlight of the morning was that I rang the Minister's Secretary three times while we were talking.

GINA ı How did you manage that?

JOHN ı He bumps his redial button. He rang me a couple of times the other night from an extremely enjoyable time. There you go, he's done it again.

BRYAN *(On phone)* ı Hello. Hello. Oh hi, Nicholas, hi, yes, Bryan. I was just ringing to say that I thought the host cities idea was the go.

GINA ı That's not what you said to us.

BRYAN ı I'm sorry. Just a sec. *(He glowers at Gina)* No, Gina just wanted to know something about budgets. Yes. No. Nice talking to you, too. No other reason.

GINA *(To John)* ı He's very good, isn't he?

JOHN *(To Gina)* ı Excellent. Yes, the host cities thing was the go, yes, very much so. Bryan, give him our regards.

BRYAN ı John's just sending his regards.

JOHN ı Thank your mother for the mouse trap, Nicholas.

BRYAN ı Okay Nicholas. All right. Nice talking to you. Bye bye. Okay. God, they're useless things.

JOHN ı You want to get that bloody thing fixed, you do. That is ridiculous. *(Picks up Bryan's phone and presses the redial button)* Hello. Yes, John here. How did your meeting go with Bryan about the host cities? He seems terribly impressed. Good outcome, was it Nicholas? Yes. Mmm. Yes.

Interlude

Frequently Asked Questions

Gina is driving along with a member of the documentary crew with her.

CAMERA OPERATOR | What's this Internet thing?

GINA | It's a live press conference.

CAMERA OPERATOR | What, live on the Internet?

GINA | Yes, that's right. We're on in a minute. If you go and turn on your computer and get onto the Net you'll see us.

CAMERA OPERATOR | Live?

GINA | That's right. Live.

CAMERA OPERATOR | I didn't know you could do that.

GINA | Yes, it's exciting, isn't it? I'm not quite sure that John and Bryan are up to speed though. I hope Bryan is wearing the same socks, not odd ones. *(In a fit of road rage)* Come on! Get out of the way!

LATER, AS GINA INDICATED, SHE, JOHN AND BRYAN ARE SEATED
ON A COUCH, LIVE ON THE NET. THEY ARE ON THEIR BEST
BEHAVIOUR AND ADDRESS THEIR REMARKS TO THE CAMERA. ¶

JOHN ▶ We're going to answer these questions that have been sent
to us on the Internet. This is all very new to us so we're very
excited. I'd like to welcome anyone who's watching and we hope
that there's something here to interest you.

GINA ▶ Just a point there, John.

JOHN ▶ Yes, Gina.

GINA ▶ How do people send questions to us on the Internet?

JOHN ▶ With a mouse, as I understand it, Gina.

BRYAN ▶ It's all electronic, John.

JOHN ▶ Is that right, Bryan? Yes. We have a web number.

BRYAN & GINA ▶ It's a website, John.

BRYAN ▶ And that will be coming up on the screen shortly.
It should be there now.

GINA ▶ It will be up on the screen now.

JOHN ▶ Perhaps they put it up later.

GINA ▶ No, they put it up now. It's a 'super'.

BRYAN ▶ Is it up there, Bruce?

JOHN ▶ Let's assume it's there.

GINA ▶ It will be there. We're going out live. The number to call
will be there. Where is the Internet mail from, John?

JOHN (*Referring to a sheet of paper*) ▶ From America. Yes. Here's
one. Actually, this is interesting. This is just one taken at
random. This is actually about the country — Australia. What is
the population of Australia and what are its main industries?

GINA ▶ The population is about 17 million.

JOHN ▶ Yes, and we don't have any industries, as such.

GINA ▶ Well, that's not strictly true.

JOHN ▶ We are mainly a primary producer.

BRYAN ▶ That's not actually true, John. We do have manufacturing industries.

JOHN ▶ Where?

BRYAN ▶ Everywhere.

GINA ▶ There's one in Adelaide, I'm sure.

JOHN ▶ No. No, not any more. We fixed that. There was, I think, at one stage, just after the war. In fact one of us could possibly ring the government at some stage and see if we do have any manufacturing industries but essentially I've answered the question — we grow things.

GINA ▶ Primary industry.

JOHN ▶ Primary industry as well, yes.

BRYAN ▶ There are two.

GINA ▶ There's tourism.

JOHN ▶ Tourism, yes. Travel-related disciplines in the general . . . travel and tourism-indexed areas of hospitality and accommodation . . . and breakfasts . . . and those zones.

GINA ▶ Wool.

JOHN & BRYAN ▶ Wool.

GINA ▶ Beef and wool. Beef and wool, yes.

BRYAN ▶ Wool by-products.

GINA ▶ Other wool.

JOHN ▶ Yes. Wool derivatives.

BRYAN ▶ Woollen derivatives.

JOHN ▶ Woollen sheep.

GINA ▶ Vegemite.

BRYAN ▶ No that's owned by Kraft, Gina.

GINA ▶ Speedo — the swimming gear — that's an Australian company.

JOHN ▶ No, it's not. We sold that.

GINA ▶ We sold Speedo? They're the main sponsor of world swimming now.

JOHN ▶ I realise that. They're absolutely enormous but they're not owned by us any more.

GINA ▶ Not ours? Are there any other questions? I think we should move on.

BRYAN *(Reading)* ▶ 'What television do we watch?'

GINA ▶ Oh, television. Top-flight American programmes.

BRYAN ▶ American ones.

JOHN ▶ Yes. We've got 'Hogan's Heroes', 'Bewitched' is on, 'Mr Ed' is on.

GINA ▶ Well, there's a lot of crap too.

JOHN ▶ Oh, there's a bit of crap as well. Sure. Oh yes, but I think everybody is agreed that the best television in the world is generally acknowledged to be Australian television.

OFF-SCREEN, SOMEONE HANDS BRYAN A SHEET OF PAPER. HE PASSES IT ON TO GINA. ¶

GINA ▶ Absolutely. Right. I have another question here: 'What is the separation of powers?'

JOHN ▶ Ah well, this is a constitutional question. The separation of powers is a constitutional division of the two entities in which power is vested in Australia: Kerry Packer and Rupert Murdoch. If Mr Packer wants cricket, Mr Murdoch would be given Telecom. If Mr Murdoch wants rugby league, of course Kerry Packer would be given the cotton industry.

BRYAN ▶ It's pretty simple, really.

JOHN ▶ It's fairly simple.

GINA ▶ Here's another one. 'Is there a good telephone system?'

JOHN'S MOBILE PHONE RINGS. HE REACHES FOR IT. ¶

BRYAN ▶ Excellent. Absolutely superb telephone system. The digital network in Australia covers 97 per cent of the telephone area in Australia.

JOHN *(On phone)* ▶ Hello? Hello? You're dropping out. Are you still there? Hello? *(Contorts all over the couch to get some reception)*

BRYAN ▶ Which is pretty superb, really.

GINA ▶ Who was that?

JOHN ▶ I don't know. He dropped out.

GINA ▶ It's terrible around here.

BRYAN ▶ John, there's another question I've got here. 'What do people do if they want us to answer questions?'

JOHN ▶ Very good point. If you would like us to answer any questions on the Internet, perhaps we could settle an argument, or maybe you'd like to make a booking, or perhaps you're just curious, this is how you get in contact with us: 'dot com'.

BRYAN AND GINA LOOK PERPLEXED. ¶

BRYAN ▶ What's 'dot com', John?

JOHN ▶ What is 'dot com'? I was told you 'dot com' — you put the mouse through the window in the 'dot com'.

BRYAN ▶ No, no, no.

JOHN ▶ And you click on it and it comes through the service station. And you choose the search motor and there's a drop-down dinner.

BRYAN ▶ John, John if I could just interrupt there, 'dot com' is not the whole address.

GINA ▶ No, no, no, and sometimes it's 'dot net' — that's the website or the URL.

BRYAN ▶ Yes, yes, you see, the 'com' comes on the end. We're talking here about the 'http'. The 'http' is only part of the address as well. What's the full address?

JOHN ▶ The full address is 178 Miller Street. That'd be the best thing and then we can get it couriered over.

BRYAN ▶ Couriered over?

GINA ▶ It will be on the screen now.

BRYAN ▶ Okay, what else have we got there, Gina?

JOHN ▶ Here's a question: 'do women get equal pay in Australia?'

GINA ▶ No.

JOHN ▶ Yes they do.

GINA ▶ Equal to what?

JOHN ▶ They get paid about the same, don't they? Women?

GINA ▶ Do they get paid the same as men?

JOHN ▶ Does a waitress get the same as a 747 pilot, Gina? No.

GINA ▶ Does a waitress get paid the same as a waiter, John?

JOHN ▶ Bryan?

BRYAN ▶ I don't think so.

JOHN ▶ No, no, get another question.

BRYAN ▶ Sorry. Okay, we've got . . .

JOHN ▶ One each perhaps.

BRYAN DISTRIBUTES SHEETS OF QUESTIONS. ¶

BRYAN ▶ Here we go. Hang on. You take those. We've got another one coming in here. John, you'd like to take this first.

JOHN ▶ All right, well, shall we just do one each then? Okay. 'I read that your government is planning to introduce a goods and services tax. What will this do to the cost of staging the games, and how much more expensive will it be now for my husband and myself and our three children to come to Australia for the games?'

BRYAN ▶ Terrific question. Mine is, 'The World Health Organisation has said that the people with the worst health record in the world are the Aboriginal people of Australia. Is it true that the Australian Government is reducing health services to Aboriginal communities?'

GINA ▶ Mine: 'At the Kyoto Conference on the Environment, Australia refused to reduce greenhouse gas emissions and announced that it was actually going to increase greenhouse gas emissions. Does Australia have a Minister for the Environment and, if so, what does he do?' *(Looks at Bryan)* Can I have a look at the GST one?

THEY START HORSE-TRADING AMONG THEMSELVES. ¶

BRYAN ▶ Do you want to have a go at the Aboriginal health one, Gina?

GINA ▶ Would you like environment because I don't need it? Do you want Aboriginal health?

JOHN ▶ No, I think really that this is not my . . . The environment? . . . Well, I think Gina could handle this as well.

GINA ▶ Well, I've got all of them now.

BRYAN ▶ Yes, I'd do all of them.

GINA ▶ The GST. Right. Goods and Services. That is, as a lot of wealthy Australians aren't paying any tax, all Australians should pay a little bit more in their every day life to cover the shortfall. Is that right . . . ? *(Looks at John)*

JOHN ▶ Not really my area.

BRYAN ▶ No, it's not my area, either. Try the Aboriginal . . .

JOHN ▶ No, I don't think I will, thanks Bryan.

THERE IS AN AWKWARDNESS ABOUT THE WAY THIS BOLD EXPERIMENT HAS FINISHED. ON THE WHOLE, HOWEVER, IT HAS GONE AWFULLY WELL AND ANYWAY, WITH ANY LUCK NOBODY SAW IT. ¶

DEAD MAN

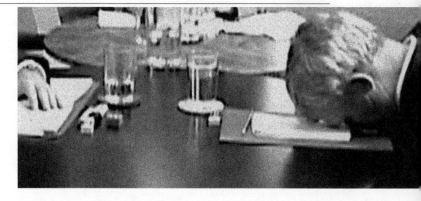

John is in an archive/storage room with the camera crew.

CAMERA OPERATOR ı John, how concerned are you about the Sydney water crisis going on until the end of the year?

JOHN ı Not very. I blame the media. Nobody grabs anything and beats it up faster than the media. I don't think there's a serious problem with Sydney water. I mean, I drink it. Unless you mean the incident the other night when somebody emptied the Olympic pool by mistake and killed a couple of hundred species of fish up in the Ryde area but that's a once-er, that's not going to happen again. *(He realises he has strayed to a point in the storage area which reveals a huge amount of bottled water. He speaks to camera)* I think we'd better reshoot this. Can we come round this way a bit? Can we come round this way a bit? Yes, now ask me again.

Gina walks into John's office.

GINA ı Are you going to do anything about this swimming programme?

JOHN ı Can you be a bit more specific, just to save time?

GINA ı This is some idiot's idea of a swimming programme. *(Puts programme in front of John)* We had the swimming programme all worked out, all organised. Everyone agreed. We tested it at the last three world championships. Now we're told it's all changed. There are going to be semi-finals because it's better for television.

JOHN ı Well, it is a consideration, isn't it? *(Looking through the programme)*

GINA ı Then I'm told there's a move on for quarter finals.

JOHN ı They work very well in tennis.

GINA ı No-one in the tennis is in six events. There's only one event *in* tennis. Then we're told they want more heats. *Now* I'm told — just now — that, in the event of a tie, they want to have a swim off!

JOHN ı Yes. What was the question?

GINA ı The swimmers are against it, FINA are against it, every swimming country is against it — we won't get them to do it.

JOHN ı Well, this is not something that I've come up with. It wasn't me who decided to turn the entire swimming programme into a single endurance event. You reckon I'm going to go to the meeting this afternoon and say 'Look, frankly I don't think you're going far enough. You haven't made the diving compulsory.

Perhaps you should make the diving compulsory before you can go in any of the swimming events'?

GINA ı I didn't say you were doing it. I just want to know what you're doing to stop it.

JOHN ı It looks to me as if someone has done a deal and I don't know quite what we can do about it.

Bryan is in a cab, scribbling in his book.

DRIVER 1 ı Who's going to win the election?

BRYAN ı I don't know.

DRIVER 1 ı Did you see the cricket?

BRYAN ı No, I was working. Who won?

Cars beep.

DRIVER 1 ı I don't know. I was working. *(To another driver)* Get out of the bloody way, you idiot!

Back at the office.

GINA ı And another thing. Why do I have to take these sleazebags out?

JOHN ı These are the IOC delegates I presume you're talking about.

GINA ı Yes. Why doesn't somebody else do it?

JOHN ı They just like to be taken out, you know, shown around the town. It's not a heck of a lot to ask.

GINA ı Yes, but why me?

JOHN ı It's a courtesy, Gina, that is extended all over the world to VIPs.

GINA ı Well, why don't you extend it, John?

JOHN ı There's a way these things are done.

GINA ı Oh, because I'm a woman.

JOHN ı It's not.

GINA ı It is.

JOHN | It's not.

GINA | It is.

JOHN | It isn't. Bryan went one night.

GINA | Bryan *and I* went one night and Bryan spent two hours playing the pokies and then went home.

JOHN | It's what is expected, Gina.

GINA | You can get someone else to do it. I'm not doing it any more.

JOHN | Have a look around you. Look about you. Who is going to do it? Who can?

GINA | No women.

JOHN | No, that's not what I'm saying.

GINA | No, that's what *I'm* saying. This IOC bloke.

JOHN | Yes?

GINA | *You* take him out.

JOHN | Oh, he doesn't want to go out with me, Gina.

GINA | Of course he does. He's bisexual. He'll love it.

JOHN | I beg your pardon?

GINA | It's a courtesy, John. It happens all over the world.

JOHN | Listen, I'm not bisexual.

GINA | I don't care what you are. I'm not being groped by any more sleazebags.

JOHN | I don't know how to work . . . *(To Nicholas)* Oh, good morning. How are you?

NICHOLAS | Good morning. I'm good. *(To camera crew)* Look, I'm sorry. You people, do you mind giving me a few minutes with John and Gina? *(To John)* I'm fine. I'll be with you in a minute. *(To Gina)* How are you, Gina?

JOHN | What's the matter?

NICHOLAS *(To camera crew)* | Thank you.

Nicholas ushers John and Gina into an office and shuts the door.

JOHN | What are you doing here?

NICHOLAS ı I'll be with you in a second, John. No worries. *(To crew)* Thank you very much. Thank you. Thank you.

The door is shut but their voices are audible.

JOHN ı What's the problem?

GINA ı What's happening?

NICHOLAS ı We have a crisis. A serious crisis.

JOHN ı What are you doing here? Does the Minister know you're here?

NICHOLAS ı I've just come from the Minister.

JOHN ı Would you like to sit down?

NICHOLAS ı No, I won't, thank you. *(He sits down)* Look, you're probably aware that there's an IOC delegate in town.

GINA ı Yes. We were just talking about him.

NICHOLAS ı He's here to attend a formal dinner tonight at Darling Harbour.

GINA ı We know that.

JOHN ı We were just discussing who might attend the dinner with the delegate.

NICHOLAS ı He's dead.

JOHN ı I beg your pardon?

NICHOLAS ı He was found dead in his hotel room at four o'clock this morning.

JOHN ı How dead?

NICHOLAS ı Well, completely dead.

JOHN ı No, how is he dead? How does he come to be dead?

GINA ı What did he die of?

JOHN ı Exactly.

NICHOLAS ı Well, it doesn't matter what he died of.

GINA ı It may have some bearing on the discussion we were having prior to your tragic arrival.

Phone rings outside the closed room.

JOHN ⏐ Will someone answer the phone? Where is Jarrod?

GINA ⏐ I don't know.

NICHOLAS ⏐ Is that the guy on the desk?

GINA & JOHN ⏐ Yes.

NICHOLAS ⏐ I gave him the day off.

JOHN ⏐ You did?

GINA ⏐ Why?

NICHOLAS ⏐ All I'm asking you to do is look after this man until the formal dinner tonight, all right?

JOHN ⏐ Look after him? He's dead, isn't he?

GINA ⏐ Why can't you look after him?

NICHOLAS ⏐ His wife and family think he's flying into Sydney this afternoon.

JOHN ⏐ Yes, why don't you look after him?

NICHOLAS ⏐ All I'm asking you to do is to look after an IOC delegate.

GINA ⏐ Why don't you look after him?

NICHOLAS ⏐ Because he's not supposed to be anywhere where he can be seen. He's not even supposed to be here. And he's *dead!*

JOHN ⏐ Why can't SOCOG look after him or something? Why us?

NICHOLAS ⏐ He's got to be kept out of the way and safe, and this is the safest place.

GINA ⏐ Safest for whom? He's dead! Oh, safest for you.

NICHOLAS ⏐ Look, all I'm asking you to do is to keep him here. I'm not asking you to do anything else. Please.

Bryan gets out of the taxi. Jasmine runs up to him. She has an open newspaper in her hand.

JASMINE ⏐ Ooh, ooh. Bryan!

BRYAN ⏐ Oh, hi Jasmine.

JASMINE ׀ Have you seen this?

BRYAN ׀ Which article?

JASMINE ׀ No, no, the ad.

BRYAN *(He describes what he is being shown)* ׀ A large advertisement warning consumers to be wary of any organisation that claims to be associated with the Olympics but is not, in fact, associated with the Olympics. All of this accompanied by a cartoon of a large kangaroo who appears to be winking at me.

JASMINE ׀ Ambush marketing.

BRYAN ׀ What is?

JASMINE ׀ This.

BRYAN ׀ Sorry?

JASMINE ׀ Large international corporations pay huge sums of money to be the official sponsors of the games. Now, invariably what happens is that their competitors attempt to confuse the marketplace by portraying themselves in such a way as to create an impression in the minds of the unwitting public that they, too, are officially connected to the Games. That, my friend, is ambush marketing.

Let me give you an example. McDonald's pay a fortune to be known as the official restaurant to the Olympic Games, but do you know that after the Atlanta Olympics 40 per cent of the American public thought that it was KFC? So you see the problem?

BRYAN ׀ Can't see the problem. What's the problem?

Bryan enters the building and heads for the lift, with Jasmine in hot pursuit.

JASMINE ׀ Look, look, Bryan, Bryan. If KFC gets, say, Carl Lewis to endorse their product the potential for confusion in the marketplace is absolutely enormous.

BRYAN ׀ Oh come on, how? What are they going to do? Get Carl Lewis to hold up a chicken and say 'This is a hamburger'?

JASMINE ׀ No. Don't be silly. They're going to get Carl Lewis to say 'Eat KFC'.

BRYAN ׀ Oh come on. Surely, surely, even given the presence of the great Carl Lewis, it is very difficult to confuse poultry product with a Big Mac, until you've eaten one.

JASMINE *(Disappointed in Bryan's failure to grasp an important distinction)* ׀ Oh, Bryan.

Back at the meeting with Gina, John and Nicholas.

GINA ι I presume he's going to die at the dinner.

NICHOLAS ι He's going to have a heart attack in the toilet. Yes, that part is taken care of.

JOHN ι Why can't he have been in Brisbane or something?

NICHOLAS ι I'm not asking you to do it, I'm telling you. Okay?

JOHN ι Why don't you tell us what actually happened?

GINA ι How long has he been in Sydney?

NICHOLAS ι He's been here a week.

GINA ι Where has he been?

NICHOLAS ι He's been in the Cross.

GINA *(To John, in a stage whisper)* ι This is the visiting dignitary you wanted me to show around town.

JOHN ι Yes, yes. What did he die of?

NICHOLAS ι Why do you keep asking me? I don't know. All I know is he was found in his room at four o'clock this morning.

GINA ι Anyone with him?

NICHOLAS ι Yes. There was evidence he'd had a guest.

GINA ι Nice. Drugs?

NICHOLAS ι I don't know.

GINA ι Guess.

JOHN ι I don't know that this is what we do, is it? Sequester the dead?

NICHOLAS ι Would you like to know what happened to the body at 5.30 this morning?

GINA ι Yes.

JOHN ι What?

NICHOLAS ι It was put in that office, there.

GINA & JOHN *(Alarm bells)* ι That's *Bryan's* office.

JOHN ι What's he doing in there?

GINA ⏐ How could you even get *in here at all?*

Gina and John walk out of the room towards Bryan's office. They make out the back of someone's head, slumped against the glass.

GINA ⏐ Oh, Jesus!

The camera crew has been trying to sneak back into the room. John is incensed and comes and speaks to them.

JOHN ⏐ Look, you're not fooling anybody. I've been watching you filming from in there and I don't mind it because we might have a problem here and I don't mind it being on record. But I want your understanding that that is not going on television. Is that all right?

CAMERA OPERATOR ⏐ Yes.

JOHN ⏐ I want your word as an Australian journalist that won't appear on television.

CAMERA OPERATOR ⏐ Okay, John. Sure.

JOHN ⏐ Good. *(Goes back into room and slams door behind him)* This is fucking hopeless. You can't bring dead people into people's offices.

GINA ⏐ I think you can. Look.

Jasmine and Bryan are now in the lift.

JASMINE *(Pointing to ad in the paper)* ⏐ It is not the quality of the ad that is the problem.

BRYAN ⏐ So what's the problem?

JASMINE ⏐ The problem is that Seed On Ground is not actually the official Olympics advertising agency.

BRYAN ⏐ Has it said here that they are the official advertising agency of the games?

JASMINE ⏐ No.

BRYAN ⏐ So, what have they done wrong other than to point out nobly and at their own expense to the citizens of Sydney the problems of ambush marketing?

JASMINE ⏐ Bryan?

BRYAN ı What?

JASMINE ı Who is going to pay to be associated with the Games when no-one can actually tell who's officially associated and who isn't?

Gina, John and Nicholas are still in the room.

GINA *(On mobile phone)* ı Yes, the President's arriving at 1.15. When's she coming? Oh good grief!

NICHOLAS ı I didn't put him in there.

JOHN ı You didn't?

GINA *(Still on phone)* ı I thought she was coming tomorrow. Oh no! When did that happen because that is a complete and utter nightmare.

John spots Bryan walking in with Jasmine and tries to prevent him from reaching his office.

JOHN ı Oh Bryan, Bryan.

NICHOLAS ı Hello Bryan, how are you?

BRYAN ı Hello, Nicholas.

JOHN ı Nice to see you. *(To Jasmine)* Do you know Nicholas, the Minister's Secretary? This is Jasmine . . .

NICHOLAS ı No, I don't.

JOHN ı How are you, Bryan? Do you want a cup of coffee? Nice cup of tea?

GINA *(Hangs up phone)* ı This is a nightmare. President Mandela is arriving, Princess Caroline's plane's flying in ten minutes late.

JOHN ı President Mandela's coming here?

Gina realises Bryan might head for his office and ushers him and Jasmine in the other direction.

GINA ı Bryan, Jasmine, why don't you two go to the airport and pick them up? They've got a tour of the Main Stadium and then the dinner at Darling Harbour tonight.

JASMINE ı Oh, love to. Do you know that he's written a book?

Bryan is less impressed at being shunted outside again.

GINA ı Yes, he has. I'll call airport protocol and tell them you're on your way. Thanks, Bryan.

JASMINE ı He probably wrote the book when he was in prison. He was in prison for 27 years.

JOHN ı Good on you, Bryan.

GINA ı Good on you.

JOHN ı They'll realise you're coming. *(To Gina)* That is brilliant.

GINA ı Thank you.

JOHN ı I take my hat off to you.

Tuesday 11.22 a.m. Bryan and Jasmine are on their way to Sydney Airport.

BRYAN ı Who's going to win the election?

DRIVER 2 ı Don't know, mate.

BRYAN ı You watch the cricket?

DRIVER 2 ı No, I didn't. I was working. Who won?

BRYAN ı Don't know. I was working. *(Yells out the window to a car)* Get out of the way, you bloody idiot!

JASMINE ı Bryan?

BRYAN ı What?

JASMINE ı They're going to come through the customs hall into half the country's waiting media. We're going to have to get them out of there very fast or they'll never get out alive.

BRYAN ı Maybe I should ring the Protocol Officer at the airport and see if we can get them out another way.

JASMINE ı Good idea, Bryan.

BRYAN ı I hate it when you ask for special treatment. *(Pulls out his mobile phone and starts dialling)*

JASMINE ı You're not asking for special treatment, you're asking for normal treatment, just the 22-carat version.

BRYAN ı Special treatment.

JASMINE ı Normal treatment, Bryan, in a special way. Would you like me to talk to them, Bryan?

BRYAN ı No, no, no, Jasmine. I will. *(Plane flies by overhead)* Hello. Hello. Hello. Hello. Hello. I can't hear a thing.

Back at the office.

GINA *(On the phone)* ı Yes. I actually think Bryan was looking after that. I'll have a look on his desk and I'll get back to you. Okay. Bye. *(Enters Bryan's office and sees the IOC delegate slumped on a chair)* Oh! *(Backs out and shuts door quietly)*

JOHN *(From his office doorway)* ı Are we going to get an agreement about this schedule?

GINA ı Oh, I don't know. Everyone agrees it stinks. You know what meetings are like. Who knows what's going to happen?

JOHN ı Well, look, just leaving the swimming out of it, what's this in the agenda about shooting, fencing and badminton?

GINA ı You've noticed that. They want to put the track, the skeet shooting, the badminton and the fencing all at the main venue.

JOHN ı Out here?

GINA ı Yes.

JOHN ı How are they going to do that?

GINA ı They're going to make them night events. They're going to put them on after everything else is finished.

JOHN ı But people will get shot, won't they?

GINA ı Well, they say they're going to fire above their heads.

JOHN ı It's never been a terribly convincing defence. 'We were firing above their heads, Your Honour, and then we noticed large numbers of deceased persons.'

GINA ı Well, they say they're going to fire the targets out over about there and they'll clear those sections out.

JOHN ı Oh yes, they'll clear those sections out. At least those sections. You're not going to be able to see much, though. Think about the badminton. It's going to look about that *(Tiny gap between his fingers)* big down here. It'll be like watching sea horses getting fluff out of one another's whiskers about a quarter of a mile off the coast.

GINA ı You know why they want to do it?

JOHN ı I don't know why they want to do it. Why do they want to do it?

GINA ı They've got all the cameras there, they've got all the lights there, why not have all the events there?

JOHN ı But it's not going to work. I mean, have you ever played badminton outside? You've got to keep getting the shuttlecock out of the neighbours' joint when there's no wind at all. What are they going to do if it rains?

GINA ı I agree. It's insane.

JOHN ı No, it can't happen. It's just ridiculous. Who's actually coming to this meeting?

GINA ı The Minister, which means his secretary — and you know what he thinks — you, the head of the Swimming Federation and me representing the Athletics Association.

JOHN ı Well, that's three–one against these proposed changes.

GINA ı How many is that?

JOHN ı For a quorum we'd need one more. Someone from SOCOG or the IOC would be good.

Penny drops. They have an IOC delegate in their office and he's not very busy. Gina and John go into full Machiavellian mode.

GINA ı What time's the meeting?

JOHN ı The meeting's at 12 o'clock, here, officially.

GINA ı Do you think we could have it earlier?

JOHN ı Yes, I think that would be a very good idea. Would you be prepared to represent the Swimming Federation as well as the Athletics Federation?

GINA ⏐ I would not only be prepared to, it would be an honour. I'd have to get the proxy.

JOHN ⏐ I think you should do that quite quickly. Because obviously the reason we would have to hold this meeting earlier is that so many of these people at the meeting would be going on to the IOC dinner.

GINA ⏐ The dinner. That's right. Well, it's important this stuff gets thrown out.

JOHN ⏐ That's right. I think this is the only way to do it.

GINA *(On phone)* ⏐ Hello, Rosa, is Don there please? It's all right, isn't it? We've got to look after him.

JOHN ⏐ Yes, he might as well make himself useful.

GINA ⏐ Don, Gina.

Graham Cousin walks in. He has the good fortune to be a journalist.

JOHN ⏐ Hello.

GRAHAM ⏐ Graham Cousin. Sorry to disturb you.

JOHN ⏐ No, no. We were sufficiently disturbed prior to your arrival.

GRAHAM ⏐ I've got an interview with the IOC bloke you've got here.

JOHN ⏐ What IOC bloke have we got here, Graham? *(John begins to usher him out)*

GRAHAM ⏐ The IOC bloke you've got here — he's going to the dinner tonight. I'm interviewing him at 11.30. Sorry, I'm a bit early, but I got finished with the other thing I was doing so I thought I'd just rock up here.

JOHN ⏐ I don't think we've got an IOC bloke here. Who told you we had an IOC bloke here, Graham?

GRAHAM ⏐ They said at the Minister's office he'd be here all day.

JOHN ⏐ Did they? And what time are you supposed to be seeing him?

GRAHAM ⏐ 12 o'clock.

JOHN ⏐ Yes, we did have an IOC person here earlier in the day, Graham, but he's out at the moment. He probably won't be back for a bit. Could you come back at 1? What time is your deadline?

GRAHAM ⏐ Oh, about 2. That's cool. I'll come back at 1 then.

JOHN | Yes, good, Graham. Come back at 1.

GRAHAM | See you at 1 then.

JOHN | Yes. Good.

CAMERA OPERATOR | What was that all about, John?

JOHN (*To camera*) | That's about the fourth thing we've got to deal with this morning.

At Sydney Airport.

BRYAN | I don't know what you're doing up in Marketing but we are very busy.

JASMINE | Look, Bryan, the fact is that ambush marketing is a reality.

BRYAN | Oh, spare me.

JASMINE | No, look.

BRYAN | Spare me, Jasmine.

JASMINE | In the lead-up to the Atlanta Olympics the Ford Motor Company in America ran a television commercial showing a man rowing a boat down a river.

BRYAN | What has that got to do with it?

JASMINE | Rowing!

BRYAN | I know that.

JASMINE | It's an Olympic sport.

BRYAN | I realise that.

JASMINE | And the Ford Motor Company is not an official Olympic sponsor.

BRYAN | Jasmine, what I'm saying is what has rowing got to do with selling bloody cars?

JASMINE | It's the clever association between an Olympic sport and a product, at a time when the Olympics is in the forefront of everybody's mind.

BRYAN | Brilliant! Brilliant!

JASMINE | It is. It is. That's the point.

BRYAN | If the way to sell cars is to show people a boat going down a river, there's going to be a boom in public transport. Unbelievable!

Brett Paine, the airline Protocol Officer, comes up and introduces himself.

BRETT | Bruce!

BRYAN | Sorry?

BRETT | Bruce?

BRYAN | Bryan.

BRETT | Bryan, Brett.

BRYAN | Oh, Brett.

BRETT | And Jasper?

JASMINE | No, Jasmine.

BRETT | You've got Prince Charles arriving.

JASMINE | Princess Caroline.

BRETT | And President Wilson Brook-Taylor.

BRYAN | President Nelson Mandela, the South African President.

BRETT | Look, you've got Nelson Mandela coming too. I love him. And Princess Caroline of Monaco.

BRYAN | Yes, we're here to meet them. *(Offers to shake Bryan's hand)*

BRETT | Yes, Brett. How are you?

BRYAN | Good.

JASMINE | Where can we meet them?

BRETT | Sorry, I'm a little bit deaf. I've been working here for about two years.

BRYAN | We're here to meet them off the plane.

BRETT | No. Not yet. They'll still be on the plane. They're actually coming on different flights.

JASMINE *(Slowly)* | Yes, but they're arriving at about the same time.

BRYAN | Yes, Jasmine. It's a big country. I'm sure we can fit them both in.

BRETT | Something to do with the Olympics.

BRYAN | Yes.

JASMINE *(Slowly)* ⏐ Yes. We're taking them on a tour of the Olympic Stadium.

BRYAN ⏐ Yes, but it won't be together.

JASMINE ⏐ What?

BRYAN ⏐ Well, protocol dictates that the Princess, being royalty, gets precedence.

BRETT ⏐ Manchester United, I think. Three nil.

JASMINE ⏐ No, no, no.

BRYAN ⏐ What do you mean?

JASMINE ⏐ We'll be taking the President first. He's the Head of State.

BRYAN ⏐ Hang on. She has a lineage that goes back eight centuries.

JASMINE ⏐ He is a world hero.

BRYAN ⏐ She's never been in jail.

JASMINE ⏐ He went to gaol for what he believed in.

BRYAN ⏐ She's more famous than he is.

JASMINE ı Mandela is older.

BRETT ı You do realise that they're coming on different flights, don't you?

BRYAN & JASMINE ı Yes, we do.

BRETT ı And that neither is flying with this airline?

BRYAN ı I beg your pardon?

JASMINE ı But . . . you are the official Olympics carrier.

BRETT ı They should be, because we are the official Olympics carrier.

BRYAN ı Hang on.

JASMINE ı They're not flying with you?

BRETT ı No.

BRYAN ı They're not coming in on the official airline?

BRETT ı Where?

BRYAN ı Oh Jesus.

Back at the office, John and Gina are convening the meeting. John, the dead IOC delegate and Gina are in attendance.

GINA ı Welcome everybody. I'll just get started.

JOHN ı Yes.

GINA ı I move that the swimming programme be conducted as it was going to be conducted earlier, that these proposed changes be thrown out and that we revert back to the system as recommended by FINA. Do I have a seconder?

JOHN ı Yes. I second that.

GINA ı Proposed on my left, seconded on my right. Show of hands. Any objections? Unanimous.

JOHN ı Could I also move, and I do this in conjunction with my friend across the table here, that this body hears *no further applications on this question whatsoever*?

GINA ı Proposed here. Seconded here. Any objection? Carried. And now we come to the question of running the main venue as a 24-hour live television extravaganza with particular reference to the shooting, the fencing and the badminton. This is an outrage, Mr Chairman. My friend here was saying earlier that not only does this proposal, which he described as ludicrous . . .

JOHN ı Yes, it sounds ludicrous.

GINA ı It's ludicrous . . .

JOHN *(Writing)* ı Ludicrous . . .

GINA *(She continues)* ı . . . make a mockery of the games as an event which can be properly enjoyed and celebrated by the host city, it also presents a scheduling nightmare and destroys the integrity of the individual disciplines involved.

JOHN ı Yes. Did he actually ask for these very legitimate concerns to be minuted?

GINA ı He did, Mr Chairman, how perceptive of you. He was particularly appalled — please get this down — that the games seemed to be turned into a benefit for television, a notoriously greedy and selfish medium that is obsessed with money and sensation. Is often run by morons who wouldn't know if their arses were on fire unless the ratings told them so.

JOHN ı Excuse me. Excuse me. You've lost me a bit. Go back — greedy and selfish industry. Arses on fire. Morons.

GINA ı Morons: M–O–R– . . .

JOHN *(Writing)* ı Run by morons, many of whom are insane.

At the airport.

BRYAN ı Nelson Mandela's coming in on South African Airlines and Princess Caroline is coming in on Alitalia Airlines.

JASMINE ı Bryan, the press have to see them coming through the Ansett door.

BRYAN *(To Brett)* ı Can you get them both to come through the Ansett airlines door?

BRETT ı No, I can't. There's no connecting building.

JASMINE ı The press cannot see them coming through another airline.

BRYAN ı Can we get them to come through the back? Out the back?

BRETT ı No, they're coming in from overseas. They have to go through customs.

JASMINE ı Well, you get them from customs and you take them out through the rental car exit.

BRETT ı But they're in two other buildings.

BRYAN ı You go to one and we'll go to the other.

JASMINE ı We'll get Princess Caroline and you meet us at Rent-a-car. Rent-a-car.

BRYAN ı I think he understands us.

JASMINE ı I don't think he heard me. He won't know where we are, Bryan.

At the meeting in the office.

GINA *(Peering at the dead man)* ı He gives me the creeps.

JOHN ı He's only trying to do his best. Any further business? No? There being no further business the meeting closed at 12.45. Thanks for your attendance, one and all.

GINA ı No, thank you.

NICHOLAS *(From afar)* ı Hello. Hello.

GINA ı Hello.

NICHOLAS ı Sorry I'm late.

GINA ı What for?

NICHOLAS ı The meeting.

JOHN ı Hello.

NICHOLAS ı Isn't there a meeting about the swimming schedule?

Back at the airport, Bryan and Jasmine are bluffing their way through into a different part of the airport.

BRYAN ı Just flip it open. Just flip it open. *(To guard, while brandishing open wallet like a badge)* Federal Police.

JASMINE *(To guard, while brandishing open wallet like a badge)* ı Mittagong Regional Library.

Guard prevents the camera crew from going with Bryan and Jasmine.

Gina and John are in the office with Nicholas. Gina and John are looking very pleased with themselves.

NICHOLAS ı How are things with . . .?

JOHN ı Pretty good, thanks. Yes, I think we've had not a bad day.

NICHOLAS ı Right, well, I'll have a cup of coffee, I think.

Graham Cousin returns.

JOHN ı Yes, get a cup of coffee. *(To Graham)* Graham!

GRAHAM ı Sorry, I'm a bit early.

JOHN ı Oh Graham. How are you?

Gina runs off and starts talking in a loud voice, ostensibly to the IOC bloke.

GINA ı No, no. You listen to me. What I'm saying is, you cannot have the games without television. Are you insane? No please, have the decency to listen to me. I listened to you. You listen to me.

John closes the door and confides in Graham.

JOHN | There've been a couple of issues crop up in your absence, Graham. I'm afraid the IOC bloke's going to have to leave here. There's a chopper coming for him in a couple of minutes. He's going out to the rowing. He apologises for inconveniencing you and he was most particular that I give you this and that you don't show it to anyone else.

GRAHAM | What is it?

JOHN *(In a whisper)* | This is the minutes of a meeting that was held here this morning. As a result of this meeting, Graham, the changes to the swimming schedule are dead. The proposal to run this venue as an all-night venue is gone. All of them are completely out and nobody will get a copy of that until tomorrow morning. You'll be the only journalist in the place with a copy of that.

GRAHAM | It's all in here, is it?

JOHN | All in there, Graham.

GRAHAM | Thank you very much.

JOHN | Well, that's a great pleasure, Graham.

GRAHAM | Thank you. I'll see you later.

JOHN | Yes.

Nicholas points to the room where Gina is still talking. He looks at John quizzically and his nose tells him there is a rodent in the building.

At the airport, Jasmine and Bryan manage to get Princess Caroline and President Nelson Mandela into a waiting taxi with Brett Paine's help.

Back at the office, John and Nicholas carry the IOC delegate out of the meeting room. They knock his head against the doorframe.

NICHOLAS *(To camera)* | Would you have some respect, please?

JOHN | Have some respect! You're a bit rich, aren't you? You're happy for him to sit in Bryan's office all day. You've lied to his wife and family, you're going to prop him up in a dunny at a cocktail party and you want them to show some respect! What are they going to shoot? They haven't got any choice, for God's sake. Come on, pal.

Camera pans to Gina, who distracts the crew by tap-dancing.

JOHN ı Gina, are you coming?

They all enter the lift. The taxi with the foreign dignitaries pulls up just as they are hauling the body out.

JOHN ı Oh God, who's that?

GINA ı It's Bryan.

NICHOLAS ı Just prop him in the comer.

JOHN ı Hello, Bryan, how are you?

BRYAN ı I'm good. How are you?

JOHN ı Having a good day?

BRYAN ı Yes, not bad. Are you going back up to the office?

JOHN ı No, we're not, Bryan, as it happens.

BRYAN ı Can we hide a couple of people up there?

GINA ı Pretty much up to pussy's bow with hiding people . . .

JOHN ı Where are they going, Bryan? Where are they going?

BRYAN ı President Mandela and Princess Caroline.

JOHN ı Where are they going?

BRYAN ı They're going to a big cocktail party at Darling Harbour.

JOHN ı Nicholas can take them. Nicholas and his mate are going down there now.

NICHOLAS ı No.

GINA ı Yes, come on.

NICHOLAS ı No, I am not.

JOHN ı You're going down to the cocktail party.

The IOC delegate is assisted into the taxi.

NICHOLAS ı In the front. In the front.

GINA *(To the foreign guests)* ı Welcome to our beautiful city.

JOHN ı He's had a few but . . . Darling Harbour. Mr Mandela. Thank you, Mr President.

GINA ı Princess Caroline. Love your mother's work.

JOHN ı Have a good night, Nicholas.

JASMINE ı Have a lovely night.

JOHN ı Lovely to see you looking so well.

Taxi pulls away. It is a Legion Cabs vehicle. John pulls his phone out of his pocket and dials for Legion Cabs.

JOHN ı Yes, Legion Cabs, good. How would you like to become the official carrier to the Olympics? Yes? I think we've got a deal.

J'ACCUSE

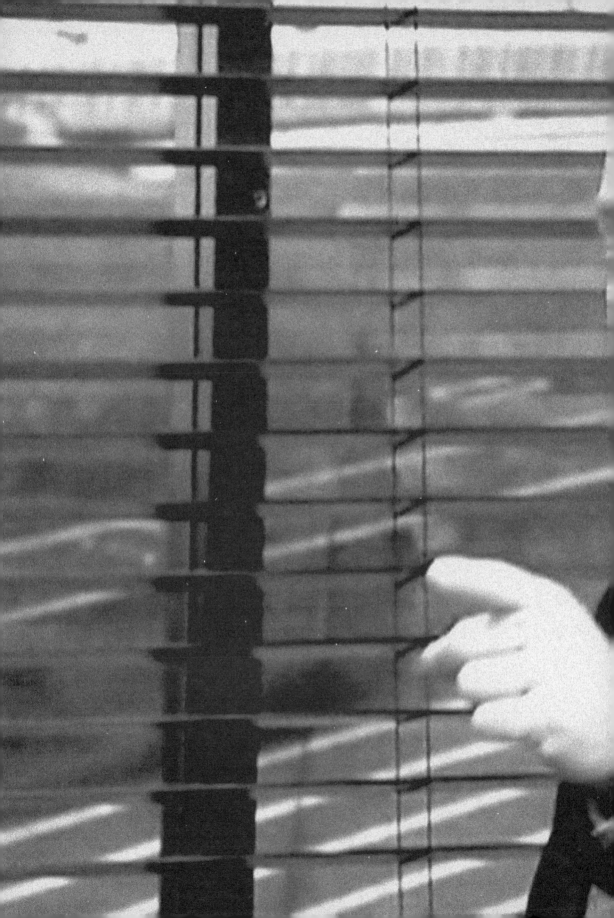

John finds that when it comes to being interviewed, the thrill is gone.

CAMERA OPERATOR ⏐ John, how are things going in terms of ticket sales? The power in Auckland, the water in Sydney and now the gas in Melbourne.

JOHN ⏐ Righto! Cut! I've just about had it with the press setting the agenda. I said I wouldn't talk about that. You'll have to leave. I've got other fish to fry. Go on. I've got things to do.

Thursday 10.46 a.m. The office is abuzz with people hard at work. John is walking towards Gina's office. He reads from a newspaper.

JOHN ⏐ Gina, listen to this: 'The so-called Games of the 27th millionairium are now a staggering $248,000 a day over budget and we have on our hands a full-scale corporate catastrophe in which the loss of the *Titanic* could quite happily be written off as office stationery. Once a celebration of youth and now little more than an orgy of waste and incompetence, haemorrhaging money and run by the biggest pack of no-hopers anyone could find anywhere, these Olympics have become an embarrassment to all thinking Australians.'

GINA ⏐ What about the rest of us?

JOHN ⏐ 'There is something rotten in the state of SOCOG' — a Shakespearian reference — 'as one highly placed source inside the organisation has said, if this were a private company there would have been a fire here last Thursday.' What idiot wrote this?

GINA ⏐ Jack Hughes.

JOHN ⏐ Well, look, he hasn't checked any facts. In fact there aren't any facts in here. This is just opinionated drivel.

GINA ⏐ He writes for the most respected newspaper in the country.

JOHN ⏐ We can't have this sort of rubbish being written. This is badly written, completely unresearched rubbish.

GINA ⏐ You don't mind badly written, unresearched rubbish when it's on your side.

JOHN ⏐ I don't have a problem with favourable crap. Favourable crap is an excellent result. It's the best result you can get in Australia, favourable crap.

GINA ⏐ We can't control the press, John.

JOHN ⏐ Well, we're not having the press control us. Who is this genius? I think we might get him in.

GINA ı Bad idea. Bad idea.

JOHN ı We could have him killed.

GINA ı Look, it's a free country. He can write whatever he likes.

JOHN ı I'm not having him write it about us.

GINA ı The Minister called. Are you going to a meeting about drug testing?

JOHN ı Yes, I am. In fact you can wise me up about this. The current drug regimen is still random drug testing, isn't it?

GINA ı Why is the Minister calling a meeting about drug testing?

JOHN ı He's going to make an announcement.

GINA ı What sort of announcement? Is he thinking of replacing the current system?

JOHN ı Yes, perhaps.

GINA ı In what way?

JOHN ı Possibly. Well, you know everybody wants a drug-free Olympics. And as you yourself would be aware — in fact you've told me this yourself — the current system doesn't really work terribly well.

GINA ı The current system isn't perfect but it's the best system we've got.

JOHN ı But it takes ages, it's subject to all sorts of mess ups — there have been all sorts of samples being tampered with — it's invasive. I don't know why that system was adopted in the first place.

GINA ı The Minister agreed to adopt the same system that was used in Atlanta.

JOHN ı Well, he's changed his mind now. He now realises that system is inadequate.

GINA ı Well, at least we know this one works.

JOHN ı Oh, you won't have a problem with the new one. *(He hands his newspaper to the receptionist)* Scott, would you mind ringing this bloke, Jack Hughes, and asking him if he wouldn't mind coming and seeing me at some point?

GINA ı New one? What new one?

JOHN ı Just excuse me for one moment. *(He goes towards Bryan's office. Gina gives up and goes back to her office to get some work done)* Bryan! Bryan, why isn't the lacrosse centre finished?

BRYAN ı Lacrosse centre?

JOHN ı Yes, the Olympic lacrosse centre. It's up at Stanmore. I came past it yesterday afternoon. It's supposed to have been finished three weeks ago. There's not even anyone on the site. There's nothing up there. There's certainly no construction.

BRYAN ı What's a lacrosse centre? It's a paddock with a couple of goal posts.

JOHN ı No, no. This is a full complex. Look at the plans. It's got bars, it's got restaurants — I think you can stay there. There's certainly a computer centre. Have a look at the plans.

BRYAN ı Who's building it?

JOHN ı Trusty Constructions, it says on the sign.

BRYAN ı Oh, that's Dermot O'Gorman.

JOHN ı Bryan, I've got to show Juan Antonio a lacrosse centre in about three weeks. We haven't even got one. I think you'd better have a word with brother O'Gorman.

BRYAN ı Well, where is this place?

JOHN ı It's up at Stanmore. It's next to the archery centre. It's called — I can't remember its name but it's next to the archery centre and — I can't think of the archery centre's name either. Hang on a minute. *(Walks from Bryan's office towards Gina's)* Gina, you know something about archery, don't you?

GINA ı A bit.

JOHN ı What's the name of that big archery centre thing?

GINA ı The bullseye?

JOHN ı The bullseye. Thanks very much Gina, for your help in this matter.

John gives up and goes back to Bryan.

BRYAN ı John, I mean, I really . . . I've got this Senate's Estimates Committee stuff I've got to get together.

JOHN ı Well, look I can't possibly go, Bryan. You'd better go and speak to O'Gorman. I tell you what, if there's a cock-up it'll come out of your budget. *(John leaves Bryan's office)*

BRYAN *(Exasperated)* ı *Our* budget.

Gina walks into John's office to find out more about the new drug test.

GINA ı John, sorry to bother you. What is this new drug test?

JOHN ı What is it? It's a new drug test.

GINA ı How does it work?

JOHN ı You seem very interested.

GINA ı Yes, I am interested. I've spent a lot of time talking to sports organisations. We've just been through all the drug protocols for Sydney.

JOHN ı It's very simple. I did it myself. You put your hand on a plate — a glass plate — the magic machine is underneath the plate and it reads the specific gravity, I think it is, of every substance in your bloodstream.

GINA ı Every chemical of any sort?

JOHN ı Every chemical of any sort that's in your body. It actually prints it all out. You get a print-out.

GINA ı Is it reliable?

JOHN ı It's 100 per cent reliable.

GINA ı A hundred per cent?

JOHN ı Yes, it's totally reliable. That's the great advance. And the plan is to put one of these machines at the entrance to each of the venues. As the athletes go in they get tested and if they're not clean, they're out.

GINA ı Is the Minister going to announce this?

JOHN ı You bet he is. This is the clean Olympics. I mean, this is a fantastic coup. Everybody's tried to do it before. No-one else has even been able to . . .

GINA ı Shouldn't we think about this before he says anything?

JOHN ı Think about it? There's not a heck of a lot to think about. I mean, the clean Olympics — drug-free Olympics — this is what everybody's always wanted. I reckon it's absolutely fantastic. It is absolutely fantastic. *(To receptionist as he's leaving the building)* I'll be back in about an hour and a half.

Gina realises something is amiss, picks up her bag and follows John out.

GINA *(To receptionist)* ı I'll be back in about an hour and a half.

CAMERA OPERATOR *(To receptionist)* ı I'll be back in about an hour and a half.

John is waiting for the lift. Gina spots him and decides to take the stairs instead to beat him to the car. The camera operator follows Gina. When John enters the car Gina and crew are already inside.

JOHN ı Okay, what are you doing here?

GINA *(Puffing from the dash)* ı I'm going past the Minister's office. I'll drop you off.

JOHN ı Where are you going?

GINA ı Past the Minister's office. I'll drop you off. *(To Ian, the driver)* Minister's Office, thanks Ian.

Gina is still puffing, having just sprinted down the stairs.

JOHN ı Are you all right?

GINA ı Yes, I'm fine.

Thursday 11.14 a.m. Bryan is at a construction site operated by Dermot O'Gorman.

BRYAN ı John drove past it and reckons it wasn't there.

DERMOT ı Oh well, we are a bit behind schedule.

BRYAN ı My point is, is there going to be a lacrosse centre out there by next week?

DERMOT ı No. Probably not.

BRYAN ı Have you started building it?

DERMOT ı There's a shortage of skilled workers, shortage of skilled labour.

BRYAN ı What are you talking about? There are a million unemployed people out there.

DERMOT ı Bricklayers are skilled labour and we can't get any brickies.

BRYAN ı Look at the construction that's going on around town. How are they doing that? What are they doing, knitting those building? Crocheting them?

DERMOT ı No, no. Look, all I'm trying to indicate to you is there's so much construction going on in Sydney at the moment you can't get bricklayers. Two years ago there were brickies everywhere, but they were getting sixty cents a brick and now they're getting a dollar seventy.

BRYAN ꞁ Why?

DERMOT ꞁ Every developer's got a project on, you know, every hotel's putting on rooms.

BRYAN ꞁ But isn't everyone's cost based on a dollar seventy a brick?

DERMOT ꞁ Yes, and they're all over budget.

BRYAN ꞁ Well, how can they afford it?

DERMOT ꞁ They can't.

BRYAN ꞁ You've got a contract to build a lacrosse centre out there.

DERMOT ꞁ But we can't get the workers.

BRYAN ꞁ Can we get some brickies in from other states?

DERMOT ꞁ Might be able to fly someone in from New Zealand.

BRYAN ꞁ They wouldn't let them in. They'd want to use wide trowels.

DERMOT ı Is your problem the lacrosse centre or the fact that Juan Antonio Samaranch is coming here to see it?

BRYAN ı Both, really.

DERMOT ı Which one's more urgent?

BRYAN ı Well, Juan Antonio is coming out here this century.

DERMOT ı Right. The reason I ask is that my country club is right next door to one of those lacrosse things and I'd be more than happy to show him around.

BRYAN ı It's not going to solve the problem.

DERMOT ı We can't do the work if we haven't got the money.

Gina and John are in the car together and obviously have been for some time.

GINA ı Because you can't just announce that you're introducing some completely new procedure. All the sporting bodies have got to approve it. They've got to see trials. It has got to be in operation in international competition.

JOHN ı Can't think of a better example of international competition than the Olympic Games.

GINA ı John, for a new drug test to be brought in you have to get agreement from every single sporting body in advance in every competing country.

JOHN ı That'd take years.

GINA ı Exactly.

JOHN ı The clean Olympics. This is what we want. Everybody's wanted to do this but nobody's previously been able to.

Bryan is back at the office, on the phone to Hal Parkinson, an investment funds manager at a major bank.

BRYAN ı Hello, Hal? I've got a little financial thing I need to talk to you about. Yes, lacrosse centre. Okay. Yes. Could I meet you in about ten?

John and Gina are waiting for Nicholas.

GINA ı It'll keep people away from the games.

JOHN ׀ It'll keep drug cheats away from the games and that is a very, very good thing.

GINA ׀ Do you know how many big athletes are going to come if you eliminate drugs?

JOHN ׀ I know there'll be a few . . . Oh, hello Nicholas. I'll see you later, Gina.

NICHOLAS ׀ Good morning.

GINA ׀ John's asked me to come along because he's not really up to speed with drug protocol.

JOHN ׀ That's not quite right.

GINA ׀ He feels himself, quite rightly in my view, to be a complete ignoramus on the subject whereas I've spent my life dealing with it.

JOHN ׀ Not quite right. I'll see you back at the office, Gina.

GINA ׀ Do you know how many athletes are coming to the Games?

NICHOLAS ׀ We're thinking about 10,000, aren't we?

JOHN ׀ Ten thousand two hundred, or something.

GINA ׀ Ten thousand were coming. Less 30 per cent. That's 7000.

JOHN ׀ Why less 30 per cent?

GINA ׀ Because if you bring in this new test they won't all come.

NICHOLAS ׀ Thirty per cent won't come?

GINA ׀ At least 30 per cent.

JOHN ׀ Of course they'll come. Why wouldn't they come?

GINA ׀ Oh, and their sponsors won't come either, because if the athletes aren't here, their sponsors won't be here.

JOHN ׀ Sponsors will all come. Everybody's agreed about drugs in sport. Nobody wants it.

NICHOLAS ׀ No sponsors?

JOHN ׀ If people are going to cheat . . .

GINA ׀ Do you want any records broken?

JOHN ׀ Are you saying that 30 per cent of athletes are taking drugs?

GINA ׀ That has been the figure for ages. Did you see the Tour de France? They threw out a couple of entire teams.

NICHOLAS *(Passing on a message to John)* ⏐ Ring Bryan. Urgent. *(To Gina)* Thirty per cent?

John walks away to make the call to Bryan on his mobile phone.

JOHN ⏐ Excuse me a minute.

NICHOLAS ⏐ Thirty per cent? Sponsors?

JOHN *(On mobile phone)* ⏐ Hello. Yes, it's me.

Nicholas and Gina, in the meantime, move into Nicholas's office. Nicholas checks to make sure John is out of earshot.

NICHOLAS ⏐ I think it's going to be very hard to argue against the new testing. It's foolproof.

GINA ⏐ Nothing is foolproof.

NICHOLAS ⏐ Yes, but it's so good. I mean, I saw it with the Minister. You put your hand on it and it reads the chemical composition. It's a brilliant invention.

GINA | Yes, but the invention is not the issue. The issue is, do we want the world's best athletes coming to Sydney?

NICHOLAS | Well, let's say we did.

GINA | All right. In that case the test would have to undergo more trials. It would be a shame if we brought it here and there were some problems with it and the athletes had to pull out. You know, we've got a fair bit riding on this.

NICHOLAS | All right, I see your point.

GINA | It would be different if it had been used at the World Cup Athletics meets or the Pan Pacs or something like that.

NICHOLAS | Yes, we'd have a precedent then, wouldn't we?

GINA | Exactly. If there was a precedent, we wouldn't have a problem.

NICHOLAS | All right. I hear what you're saying.

GINA | Good. I don't think John does.

John walks in at this point.

NICHOLAS | Oh, I think he does. *(To John)* You do, don't you?

JOHN | Pardon?

GINA | Nicholas doesn't think you hear what I'm saying.

JOHN | I beg your pardon.

NICHOLAS | Come on. Let's do it.

JOHN | I beg your pardon, Gina.

They enter the Minister's office and Nicholas shuts the door behind them.

NICHOLAS | Good morning.

Thursday 2.48 p.m. At a café. Bryan is at a table with Hal Parkinson and Shauna McEwan. Shauna is head actuary of a major insurance company.

BRYAN | Okay, homework for today: how do we get some more money? We need extra money for a lacrosse centre. We can't ask the Minister. How would you do it at the bank?

HAL ı Well, how many budgets have you got? How many project budgets have you got?

BRYAN ı About forty.

HAL ı And you've got a Development Budget, a Project Budget and a Management Budget for each one?

BRYAN ı Yes.

HAL ı So, 120 budgets. How much do you need for this lacrosse thing?

BRYAN ı About half a million.

HAL ı Okay. Well, you add three or four grand onto each project as an over-run and that will give you four hundred grand. Then underpay all your suppliers on all projects by as much as you need to make up the other hundred K.

BRYAN ı Well, hang on a minute, you can't add money onto these budgets. *(John walks in at this point and takes a seat)* Oh, hi John.

JOHN ı Sorry I'm late.

HAL ı You don't add it all on in the one go. You're only adding little amounts. No-one will even notice.

JOHN *(To Bryan)* ı This is how you're getting the money?

BRYAN ı Yes.

HAL ı I'm just saying, you go through all your budgets, you add a few cents onto each and every item. It's all electronic. So no-one will even notice.

SHAUNA ı Typical banker.

HAL ı Well, what would you do?

SHAUNA ı Insurance is much more subtle than that.

BRYAN ı What would you do?

SHAUNA ı You'd sell services that you are not going to provide. Are you selling corporate packages?

BRYAN ı Yes.

SHAUNA ı Ticketing packages? Do they get a box up in a stand with drinks and food and so on?

JOHN ׀ Yes.

SHAUNA ׀ Make them pay extra for drinks and food. And make them pay extra for a guest.

JOHN ׀ But it's *for* guests.

SHAUNA ׀ You'll make a few bob then.

BRYAN ׀ What? Charge them for the boxes?

SHAUNA ׀ Yes.

BRYAN & JOHN ׀ They've already paid for the boxes.

SHAUNA ׀ They *think* they've paid for it.

JOHN ׀ What *have* they done?

SHAUNA ׀ They've purchased the *right* to pay for it. They've prevented anyone *else* paying for it. We'll stick it on the back of the ticket in a microscopic font. No-one will notice.

HAL ׀ You take a little bit from here, a little bit from there. You look after the pennies, the pounds take care of themselves.

SHAUNA ׀ No. You need to get money from a service you subsequently aren't going to provide.

BRYAN ׀ But why would people want to buy a service that's not going to be provided?

SHAUNA ׀ You tell them you *are* going to provide it.

JOHN ׀ But how can you not provide a service that you have undertaken to provide?

SHAUNA ׀ You provide part of it. If they want the rest they've got to pay extra.

John looks at Bryan.

JOHN ׀ It's no wonder they've got more money than we have, is it?

Bryan and Gina are in the car.

BRYAN ׀ How did the drug meeting go?

JOHN ׀ Oh good, good. *(He is looking at a brochure)* Is this O'Gorman's country club?

BRYAN ׀ Yes.

JOHN | I reckon you're going to take Juan Antonio Samaranch up here, perhaps you should do it at night.

BRYAN | Why?

JOHN | Well it's . . .

BRYAN | Not a world-class facility?

JOHN | Have you ever been up there?

BRYAN | No.

JOHN | There was an earthquake up here in 1973. It did two hundred grand's worth of improvements. *(The car hits a very corrugated road without the benefit of shock-absorbers. The rest of the discourse is conducted through chattering teeth and slightly blurred vision)* Does he know where the address is that we're going to?

BRYAN | Yes.

JOHN | Does he?

BRYAN | Yes.

JOHN | I hope he bloody knows where he's going?

Tuesday 4.26 p.m. Bryan, Nicholas and John are in a meeting.

BRYAN | Nicholas . . . we're going to have to find some money for the lacrosse centre.

NICHOLAS | The Minister has said this till he's blue in the face. He cannot see why this wasn't completed in accordance with *your* budgetary estimates.

JOHN | Well that's just ridiculous, isn't it?

NICHOLAS | Why?

JOHN | Because it's not very helpful. It doesn't actually answer the question.

BRYAN | We're sitting right on top of all our budgets and we've got cost over-runs coming out of our ears.

NICHOLAS | Whose fault is that?

JOHN | We obviously can't complete these buildings if the costs have tripled.

NICHOLAS | But that's what you're here to do. That's what these estimates are for.

JOHN | I've got to go and show Juan Antonio Samaranch a lacrosse centre.

NICHOLAS | Well, he'd better see one, hadn't he?

From this point on, the three men all talk at the same time, loudly and with feeling.

BRYAN | We haven't got one.

NICHOLAS | I understand that. You should have built one.

JOHN | What am I supposed to tell him? Should I perhaps pop down to the squash centre and pretend that it's a lacrosse centre? Should I go down there and say to him 'It looks like a squash centre. They look like squash players'?

NICHOLAS | This is happening again, again and again. It happens with sponsorship . . .

This goes on for some time. Surprisingly, no conclusion seems to be emerging when John becomes aware that someone is calling him.

RECEPTIONIST *(From outside the office)* | John, Jack Hughes. John!

John leaves Bryan's office to greet Jack Hughes.

JOHN | Excuse me a moment. *(To Jack)* Hello.

JACK | Jack Hughes.

JOHN | John Clarke.

JACK | Respected journalist.

JOHN | Yes, so I've heard. Come down into my office. Thank you very much for coming.

Meantime, in Bryan's office, Bryan and Nicholas are still slugging it out.

BRYAN | Five dollars ninety. Don't bloody get aggressive with me. Don't get aggressive with me. *(Nicholas is hurling bits of paper at Bryan)*

John's office is an oasis of calm by comparison. He addresses Jack.

JOHN | You see, if you're opposed to the Olympics we do have a fundamental problem, don't we?

JACK | I'm not opposed to the Olympics, John.

JOHN I Yes, you are. You put shit on the Olympics. That's what you do. I've read your stuff. I've been back through your stuff for the last six months and it seems to me that's pretty much what you do, Jack. You haven't got a decent thing to say about them.

JACK I I'm not even talking about the Olympics. I'm talking about all the money that's being spent on them.

JOHN I Well, we're not going to be able to put the Games on, are we, if we're not prepared to spend the money that's required to get them to the start line.

JACK I Let's not have them then.

JOHN I Well, if your position is that we shouldn't have them, I want to know why you're called the 'Official Olympics Correspondent'.

JACK I Don't try and paint me as anti the Olympics, John. I'm not anti the Olympics.

JOHN I Yes, well, you're not lobbying for them very successfully at the moment, are you?

JACK I I'm not saying anything about the fixture itself. I've got no problem with the games. I mean, look at it, John. It's supposed to have a tradition of amateurism, right? Fair play, decency. I mean this whole original event could have been held in a bloody local park for about eight dollars fifty. But what I'm talking about, John, is this great consumerfest, all set up by international business for international television, all paid for by the Australian taxpayer.

JOHN I Sure. Look, if that is your position, I suggest you make out a cogent argument in accordance with that position and you take it to the IOC. You see, you're just baying at the moon in the newspaper. Go and see the Minister. You're not being very helpful as far as I'm concerned. We here are just trying to do our job.

JACK I I'm just trying to do my job too, John. I'm getting paid to write stuff for the paper.

JOHN I What you're writing in the newspaper, frankly, is a lot of rhetorical crap. I reckon you don't even want answers to half of these questions.

JACK I I've obviously got you worried, John.

JOHN I If you've got real questions I'm confident there'll be real answers.

JACK I I've got real questions.

JOHN I Let's look at the real questions. What are they?

JACK | They'll be in Saturday's paper.

JOHN | Look, Jack, if you want to drop a fact into one of your scintillating articles at any point, you know where we are. Give us a whistle.

Jack pulls out a sheaf of paper and whistles. John accepts the challenge.

JOHN | Oh yes. What's this? This is what you're writing for Saturday, is it?

JACK | No, that's for next week.

JOHN | I see. Where did you get these figures?

JACK | I did a budget.

JOHN | We've got a budget. We sent out a budget, Jack.

JACK | Yes, I just couldn't find anything in your cost estimates that cover these expenses here. *(Points to an item on the paper)*

JOHN | Which expenses?

JACK | We're paying for all these officials to come out.

JOHN | Well, as the host nation — a technical term — we are required to pay for the athletes and officials to come out here. That's the deal, Jack, and it is all in here. If you go through here you'll find that *(He finds it)* — there you go — under Travel.

JACK | Have you costed all that out?

JOHN | Yes. That's all been costed out. That'll all be in there.

JACK | It's going to cost ten times that much.

JOHN | Why?

JACK | Do you know how many officials are coming out here, John?

JOHN | Well, yes, we do. There's an official accreditation process.

JACK | And how many accredited officials do you think are coming out from Mulravia?

JOHN | From Mulravia? I don't have that information readily to hand but I can check that out.

JACK | I can tell you. There are 24 officials coming out from Mulravia.

JOHN | Well, I would have to check that out.

JACK ı You can check it until your arse falls off. I'm telling you that's what's happening.

JOHN ı Well, you can tell me that till your dick catches fire. I'm still going to have to go check it out.

JACK ı Okay, John. Okay. Do you know how many *athletes* are coming out from Mulravia?

JOHN ı I don't know how many athletes are coming out from Mulravia, Jack, but I don't have to know that, do I, because I've got *you* here.

JACK ı Two.

JOHN ı Two.

JACK ı Two.

JOHN ı As many as that?

JACK ı Yes, 24 officials and two athletes. That's twelve officials for every athlete or, if you cut it up the other way, that's 8.33 per cent of each athlete per official.

JOHN ⅰ Yes, yes, Jack, I spent most of the morning in a meeting with the Minister on the question of the official accreditation of these people. If you had your ear to the ground you would know that and you would also recognise that the Minister might not think it very helpful for you to run that story until he's gone right through and rewritten all the accreditation procedures, which he is doing. But you're not going to hold off on that story are you, Jack, because you are a Walkley award-winning journalist.

JACK ⅰ Three times, John.

JOHN ⅰ Three times, yes.

JACK ⅰ Well, don't worry about it John, because that won't be in Saturday's paper.

JOHN ⅰ Oh, good. Well, you've got some sensitivity.

JACK ⅰ No, that's in Monday's. Cheers! *(He leaves)*

JOHN ⅰ Jesus Christ!

Thursday 6.05 p.m. Gerry Connolly is walking into the office and encounters the camera crew.

GERRY *(To camera)* ⅰ Oh, for archival purposes only, I presume.

RECEPTIONIST ⅰ Good day, Mr Connolly, John's expecting you. Just come this way. *(Leads Gerry to John's office)* John, John, Gerry Connolly's here.

John is mid-swing with a golf club.

JOHN ⅰ I beg your pardon?

RECEPTIONIST ⅰ Gerry Connolly.

JOHN ⅰ Gerry! How are you?

GERRY ⅰ You rang?

JOHN ⅰ I did. Thank you very much for coming.

GERRY ⅰ Not at all.

JOHN ⅰ Can we put you in my seat perhaps, round the other side there?

GERRY ⅰ Sure.

JOHN ⅰ Are you happy with all this?

GERRY ı Yes. Jack Hughes . . .

JOHN ı Oh, you got the fax?

GERRY ı Yeah. Who's this other bloke?

JOHN ı Juan Antonio Samaranch.

GERRY ı Juan Antonio Samaranch.

JOHN ı Samaranch, Juan Antonio Samaranch. It's a Spanish name. Okay? I've got that phone jacked up so you've just got to push 'redial' and you'll go straight through. You don't pick the receiver up and he'll just come straight through to you.

Do you want a drink of water or something?

GERRY ı No.

JOHN ı Do you mind if I stay?

GERRY ı No. Please do. *(Presses a button on the phone)* Press that, and . . . *(The phone dials and is answered)*

JACK ı Hello. Jack Hughes. Hello?

Gerry becomes Bob Hawke.

GERRY ı Jack, it's Bob Hawke, mate.

JACK ı Who?

GERRY ı Hawkey. Hazel's ex. Are you alone?

JACK ı Yes. Just hang on. I'll shut the door.

GERRY *(To John)* ı He's just shutting the door. *(Practising)* Juan Antonio Samaranch.

JACK ı Hello?

GERRY ı Correct me if I'm wrong, Jack, but you're the scribbler who's been getting into this over-budgeting crap in terms of your Olympics. *(Pretending to be talking to someone else)* Gidday mate. How are you? *(Back to Jack)* Hang on, Jack, I'm in the friggin' hotel foyer, mate, every bastard wants a root to leg in these places. *(Pretending to be talking to someone else)* Eh? There you go, mate. *(Pretending to be autographing something for a well-wisher)* Whack it on the photocopier. What's that? Not bad for an old war horse. *(Back to Jack)* You still there, Jack?

JACK ı Yes, I'm here, Bob.

GERRY ꟾ Mate, let me get to the point. I've been reading your blurbs, your articles and all your in-depth shit and that, and clearly mate, you are the only bloke who knows what's going on. These Games are a total unmitigated, bloody disgrace. Some of the plodders we've got running things at the moment couldn't organise a piss-up in a brewery.

JACK ꟾ Absolute pack of no bloody hopers, Bob.

GERRY ꟾ Well, you're onto it mate. I've been reading your stuff and you know the place is leaking idiots at the moment and it is just not going to bloody well happen.

JACK ꟾ National embarrassment.

GERRY ꟾ Well, this is what I'm indicating to you, son. Now, what I'm going to do is this. We can't be overheard, can we?

JACK ꟾ No, I'm here on my own.

GERRY ꟾ It's all hunky dory? Good. Look, Juan Antonio Samaranch has realised he's in shitter's ditch, mate, and he has pleaded with me to go in there and take over. Small team, Jack. Clear out all your galahs and, you know, get the house in order and then simply get the show on the road and get things going.

JACK ꟾ Really?

GERRY ꟾ Absolutely. Jack, mate. Reason for the call. I'm going to need someone to handle all the media on all this, son, and you're the only bloke who reads all this so let me just say this: there's a shortlist, there's one name on that shortlist and your name is on the shortlist. Are you with me?

JACK ꟾ Shit. Yes. Really?

GERRY ꟾ Okay, look Jack, I've got to skedaddle but I'll call you tomorrow night. I've got Juan Antonio Samaranch all day tomorrow . . . but Jack, don't indicate to a single living soul what I've just indicated to you until you and I get in there together.

JACK ꟾ Okay.

GERRY ꟾ Okay. Friday it'll be, but I'll call you back, Jack, and keep up the good work. Keep writing your stuff. It's shit hot.

JACK ꟾ Thanks, Bob. Cheers. Bye-bye.

GERRY ꟾ Okay, toodle-oo.

Gerry smiles and becomes Gerry again.

JOHN *(Shaking Gerry's hand)* ı You've made an old man very happy.

GERRY ı Do you think he bought it?

JOHN ı No question. I'll get you a drink tomorrow night.

GERRY ı Please.

JOHN ı Well done.

Friday 6.28 p.m. Gerry and John are in a pub. Gerry has become Paul Keating and is in the middle of telling John a story.

GERRY ı Get onto this. Get onto this. He was being recalcitrant and I said to him 'Just sit there and cop it. I'm going to do you and do you slowly' because he's up there raving and ranting — the little grub — and I said, so I said, 'Just resign, Bob. Just resign.'

Bryan and Gina come up to the table.

JOHN ı Yes. Oh hello. Good evening and welcome.

GINA ı Hi, Gerry.

JOHN ı You're familiar with most of Australia's post-war governments, aren't you?

GINA ı Certainly.

JOHN ı We're just having . . . What are we celebrating?

BARMAN ı You wanted to see the news, didn't you?

JOHN ı Oh, the news, thank you, yes. You'll have some champagne, won't you?

JOHN ı Gerry and I have got a runner in this event.

NEWSREADER ı And in news just to hand, former Prime Minister Bob Hawke has issued proceedings against the country's most respected newspaper over a story by feature writer Jack Hughes claiming the current Sydney Olympics administration was going to be removed on Friday and replaced by a management team headed by the long-serving former leader. Mr Hawke told the Press Club at lunchtime today he was confident of victory and had always wanted a large pastoral holding and an ocean-going craft of some type.

BRYAN ı What's this about?

JOHN ı Isn't that interesting?

GINA ı What have you two been doing?

JOHN ı Nothing.

GERRY ı No. Nothing.

JOHN *(Raising his glass in a toast)* ı Here's to Australian journalism.

BRYAN ı Australian journalism.

JOHN ı Yes.

GERRY ı Yes.

GINA ı Yes.

A MANAGEMENT COURSE

Friday 4.32 p.m. Three well-known logistics and infrastructure hotshots are in a bus travelling on a country road. John addresses the camera. His tone is not encouraging.

JOHN ı It's Friday afternoon and we've got three brand new sporting venues opening in Sydney on Sunday. We should be down there preparing for that but we are not. What are we doing this weekend instead?

GINA ı Bonding. *(Her tone is not encouraging either)*

JOHN ı That's right. We are going to spend the weekend in the sumptuously appointed Poxy Vistas Country Club or something.

BRYAN *(His tone is more responsible)* ı It's a conference centre.

GINA ı Oh, even better! A conference centre.

BRYAN ı It's in the Blue Mountains.

GINA ı Towards which we are currently being propelled against our will.

JOHN ı Yes, through the good offices of Kevin, a relatively harmless psychopath currently employed as a driver.

GINA ı Did you read this letter, John?

JOHN ı Yes, I did read the letter. I was very impressed with the letter.

GINA ı 'You will travel by luxury coach.'

JOHN ı Luxury coach, yes. And an ant therefore is a bird of prey.

GINA ı 'Only 60 kilometres from the city centre where you will experience intensive preparation for the problems that will inevitably arise forged in the cauldron of excitement as Olympic competition begins.' Spare me!

BRYAN ı Well, I think it will be good. I think we need it.

JOHN ı I've got a feeling I left the gas on.

BRYAN ı John, it's a training exercise, all right? Everybody's had to do it. The Organising Committee had to do it, the Ministry's had to do it.

JOHN ı Well, what is it?

GINA ı What are we being trained *as*?

BRYAN ı We're learning how to use our full potential.

JOHN ı Our full potential what?

GINA ı It will be one of those things where they say 'The Opening Ceremony's on and the power for the whole of Sydney goes off, what do you do?'

JOHN ı What do you do, as a matter of interest?

GINA ı Call an electrician?

JOHN ı Do you?

GINA ı That's what they did in Auckland.

TRAVEL GUIDE VOICEOVER ı To the left is the first wheat cairn constructed west of the Lupin. Built by Wesphalian settlers in the late 1830s, it was for many years the only gripping-centre in the humming belt and was still a fully functioning sorting-yard until about 1931. Materials for the very detailed roof were brought in by horse from as far away as Manatapanee. In the distance can be seen The Impenders, whose highest peak, Mount Anything, at 1042 feet, is one of the best examples of a basalt tangent in the region.

The yellow haze to the right of your beautifully appointed coach is created by the sulphur generated in the reaction of sunlight on spawning salmon in the streams that feed into the River Lupin. The resulting spools of upward light are unique to this area. If the moon is high, you can often witness a conjunction of igneous rock and Jupiter in the upper house. Ask your driver about how to book for the scones available from the Bide-Awee Tearooms at Ormond Bend. Thank you for travelling Aitken Coachlines.

The capital of Norway is Oslo. The valency of Carbon is 4. The margin is an area to the side of a document (qv) which is used for making notes. The quick brown fox jumps over the lazy dog. Who am I? I was born Doris Day on March 49th 1612. I rose through the ranks during the First World Environment Conference and was given my own show, 'Around We Go' in 1963. He walked on over and he asked me if I wanted to dance. He looked kind of nice and so I said I might take a chance. Brochures are available from one of our friendly 'OzSmile' Centres. Thank you for travelling Aitken Coachlines.

John and Gina seem to find the travelogue very restful and are asleep. Bryan looks out the window.

Upon arrival at the conference centre, they leave the bus and approach the building.

GINA (*To camera*) ı This is it. Are you guys coming in?

CAMERA OPERATOR ı Yes.

GINA ı Okay.

Gina reaches her room.

CAMERA OPERATOR ı Nice view, Gina.

GINA ı Yes. Ooh! Mini bar. Lovely. Want to have a drink? It's on the Olympics. Come on, let's challenge ourselves. Mmm. I think so.

Bryan is walking around the grounds.

BRYAN ı It's fantastic. You feel completely different the moment you arrive. You feel your whole mindset changing.

Meets John in a gazebo.

JOHN ı The Germans were up here, Bryan, in those trees. We were down there in those rocks. There was me, and Tiger Willis and Dusty Miller and a bloke called Stewie Davidson from Div Cav. I don't know where he came from but he was with us right through until we got out at Tobruk. God, there was some noise the night that racket went up. I thought I'd gone deaf — I hope I never have to live through anything like that again, Bryan. You young people . . . you don't know you're bloody alive.

Bryan leaves John to his soliloquy.

Saturday 9.08 a.m. Morning session is being held by Katerina Kotsonis and Miki Oikawa. Each participant is asked to be an animal. Bryan is a dog. Gina is an iguana. John is an aphid.

MIKI ı Let yourself go. You're not in the office any more. You're the animal. Let it happen. Feel it, sense it. How do they move? That's good. That's good. See how you relate to the other animals. See if you can work out what the other animals are. How do you react to them? That's right.

KATERINA ı Very good. This is good here. Be aware of the other animals around you. Let yourselves go.

Some participants are prowling around the place, following instructions. John and Gina manage to express their inner animals without resorting to movement.

Later, the formal sessions begin.

KATERINA ⏐ Firstly we'd like to thank you all for coming. And it's a great step for you all and I'd like to say congratulations and give yourselves a little clap. Fantastic. Well done. Now, you should have in your folder a brochure of the activities we'll be doing in the next two days. There are sessions and scenarios in which we will be holding here as well as outside, such as the ropes course *(Gina is alarmed by the expression 'ropes course')* and sessions in which you decide which activity is appropriate for you. Okay?

MIKI ⏐ Can we have John up here first, please?

JOHN ⏐ Here we go.

MIKI ⏐ Right, let's go to our first scenario. Here's the situation: I'm working on the gates of the main entrance of the main athletics venue. It's seven o'clock in the evening on the Thursday of the second week of competition.

KATERINA | I have a problem. I have a ticket but they won't let me in. What are you going to do about this?

JOHN | Can I ask this person questions?

KATERINA | Yes, of course.

JOHN | What is the problem with the ticket? *(To Bryan)* Bryan, can you get me a glass of water, please?

MIKI | This is not the ticket to this venue at this time.

JOHN | Why? What precisely is the actual nature of the problem with this ticket?

MIKI | This is currently the Thursday evening session of the track and field programme and this ticket is a ticket to the Thursday afternoon session. That session finished at 5.30 p.m.

JOHN | I see. *(To Bryan, who just handed him a glass of water)* Thank you very much. So what you're saying is that this person has a ticket which is not valid for this particular session?

MIKI | Correct.

JOHN | Has this all been pointed out? Is it made clear somehow on the ticket?

MIKI | Yes: 'this ticket admits holder to the session nominated on Box 4 on the obverse of this ticket and is . . .'

JOHN | I see. Which side is the obverse?

MIKI | This side.

JOHN | The side with the box on it?

MIKI | Yes, the session is nominated in the box.

JOHN | Okay, what's on the obverse of the box?

MIKI | That's the information I'm reading to you now.

JOHN | The information's on the obverse?

MIKI | Yes.

JOHN | I thought what you were reading before stated that the *box* was on the obverse of this ticket?

MIKI | Yes, well, they're both obverses.

JOHN ı They're both obverses.

MIKI ı Yes, they're obverses of each other . . .

JOHN ı You've got two obverses. That's a bit confusing isn't it? *(To Bryan again)* Any biscuits out there Bryan? I haven't had any breakfast. *(To Miki)* Sorry, I interrupted you. I beg your pardon. Continue.

MIKI ı '. . . and is not a valid ticket of entry to any other session at this or any other venue.'

KATERINA ı Are we going anywhere here?

JOHN ı I beg your pardon?

KATERINA ı Are we going anywhere? Are you making a point with this line of questioning?

JOHN ı I'm trying to establish the nature of the problem with this ticket.

KATERINA ı Yes, but time is ticking by, John.

JOHN ı Do you want me to try and solve the problem or don't you?

KATERINA ı Yes, yes of course I do but there are other crises happening at the same time. Remember, the Olympics are on. There's a full programme of events out there.

JOHN ı So what other crises have we got to deal with?

KATERINA ı Let's assume there are five other major problems.

JOHN ı Let's assume there aren't. *(Bryan returns and gives John a biscuit)* Thanks, Bryan.

KATERINA ı Let's assume that the phones are ringing.

JOHN ı Let's assume they're not. Let's assume we answered them all. Wrong numbers, a lot of them.

KATERINA ı But what are you going to do about this problem?

JOHN ı What problem?

KATERINA ı The ticket problem.

JOHN ı I don't think that is a problem.

KATERINA ı There is a problem.

JOHN ı I don't think you need a ticket to get into the venue. That's not a problem if you can get in there without a ticket, is it?

KATERINA ı That's what we've been saying. What I'm saying is I've got a ticket and I can't get into this event.

JOHN ı Yes, but you don't need a ticket to get into the event.

MIKI ı Yes, you do.

JOHN ı No, you don't. Bryan's been in and out of there twice.

KATERINA ı I'm sorry?

JOHN ı Bryan's been in and out of there twice just in the time we've been talking. He was *carrying* things and nobody stopped him. There's no security at this venue at all.

MIKI ı Why should Bryan be stopped?

JOHN ı Has he got a ticket?

MIKI ı He was bringing you glasses of water.

JOHN ı Is that what he told you?

KATERINA ı Okay. Great. Thank you very much, John. You can take a seat now.

JOHN ı I sit down now, do I?

KATERINA ı Yes, you can sit down. We'll start again.

The participants all clap as John returns to his seat. The coordinators now set their sights on Gina.

KATERINA ı Now, what's your name?

GINA ı Gina.

KATERINA ı Gina. Okay, Gina. I want to see the 800 metres. I bought a package deal — airfare, accommodation, 800 metres. I love the 800 metres.

GINA ı It isn't on till next Tuesday. That's my area.

KATERINA ı Gina, I'll put it a different way. If I bought a ticket from Hoyts to see *Titanic* in Cinema 5, have I obtained entry to *Titanic* or to Cinema 5?

GINA ı What's Hoyts?

KATERINA ｜ It's a cinema chain.

GINA ｜ Oh, the pictures. I don't go to the pictures much. I work.

KATERINA ｜ Thanks, Gina.

Katerina realises she's not going to get very far with Gina either, and tries Bryan.

KATERINA ｜ Okay, Bryan. Bryan, if I board an aeroplane to Adelaide and Perth in the belief that I boarded an aeroplane to Brisbane, I'm easily alerted, am I not?

BRYAN ｜ Absolutely . . .

KATERINA ｜ Hang on a minute, I haven't finished yet. I'm easily alerted, am I not, by Captain Umlaut who welcomes me on board the Adelaide and Perth flight? Isn't this right?

BRYAN ｜ That's right.

KATERINA ｜ Okay. Now, this isn't the situation with the Olympic tickets, is it?

BRYAN ı Well no, because there's a procedure in cases like the scenarios you've been describing about the tickets.

KATERINA ı Yes, what? Where?

BRYAN ı There's an Olympic Ombudsman at all the main venues at all times. A fully qualified legal officer who's trained in dispute resolution.

KATERINA ı Why didn't you mention this earlier, Bryan?

BRYAN ı I couldn't because John was wanting me to go out there and get him water all the time. Sorry I wasn't here when you were setting the whole thing up.

KATERINA ı Well done, Bryan.

Saturday 11.03 a.m. Gina, John and Bryan are sitting outside on the patio. Bryan has a video camera and remains keen.

GINA ı I would rather sit at home with a pencil in my eye than do that again.

JOHN ı That is a rock solid waste of time.

BRYAN ı That was very interesting.

JOHN ı I beg your pardon, Bryan?

BRYAN ı What was the name of those two actualisers?

GINA ı B1 and B2?

JOHN ı Zig and Zag?

GINA ı Bert and Patti?

JOHN ı Simon and Garfunkel?

BRYAN ı The black-haired one.

JOHN ı The Righteous Brothers?

GINA ı They both had black hair.

JOHN ı I think if you're seriously interested in that, Bryan, you're probably suffering from altitude sickness.

BRYAN ı Speaking of which.

Nicholas walks up to them, clad in a headband and mountaineering gear.

NICHOLAS ı Good morning.

GINA ı Good heavens!

JOHN ı Good Lord! There's an alpine yodelling festival, is there, in this region?

NICHOLAS ı No, I'm just prepared to have a go.

GINA ı Are you up here with us?

NICHOLAS ı No, I'm just going back. I've been here since Thursday.

JOHN ı How did you go?

NICHOLAS ı Very well. Very good. Found it useful. My team was very impressed.

JOHN ı Why?

NICHOLAS ı Because we're a mature group of people who decided to get a great deal out of the experience by putting a great deal into it. That's why, John.

GINA ı Yes, John.

BRYAN ı I agree with that entirely. I'll be back in five seconds. *(Bryan walks off)*

JOHN ı They all have headbands, do they, in your group?

NICHOLAS ı No.

GINA ı Have you done the ropes course?

NICHOLAS ı The morning or the afternoon?

GINA ı Morning.

NICHOLAS ı Yes, you've got to do it.

GINA ı What's it like?

NICHOLAS ı It's great. It's a bit steep, but it's good.

GINA ı Steep?

NICHOLAS ı Now I've got something for you. In fact have two things for you.

He hands John some documents.

JOHN ı Thank you.

GINA ı Does it involve ropes?

NICHOLAS ı No, it's a petition.

GINA ı No, the ropes course.

NICHOLAS ı Yes, it does concern itself with ropes. It is a ropes course.

GINA ı This is to prepare me for any rope climbing I might have to do, is it, in my everyday work?

NICHOLAS ı Yes, I suppose it might.

GINA ı Abseiling out for a sandwich?

John looks up from a document.

JOHN ı What is this exactly?

NICHOLAS ı The IOC has brought forward the inspection of venues meeting.

JOHN ı Brought it forward until when?

NICHOLAS ｜ Brought it forward till Monday.

JOHN ｜ Next Monday?

GINA ｜ Monday?

JOHN ｜ We're going to be up *here* till tomorrow night.

NICHOLAS ｜ That's good. You can go back nice and fresh to show Mr Samaranch all the venues. The Minister says whatever you want in the transport department you can have. Just ask me, all right?

JOHN ｜ We don't want anything in the transport department. What we need is another venue. The Minister knows this. He chaired the meeting where we discovered this — we're still one venue short.

NICHOLAS ｜ Mr Samaranch has been assured he will see all the venues. The Minister has asked me to express his full confidence, John, in your ability to satisfy Mr Samaranch and all his colleagues that all the venues for Sydney 2000 are in place.

JOHN ｜ But the Minister knows very well they're not.

NICHOLAS ｜ 'Full confidence', John, those were his words.

GINA ｜ And this petition . . . we're not allowed to deal with petitions. That's for the government.

NICHOLAS ｜ The Minister is prepared to make an exception in this case.

JOHN ｜ What is it?

NICHOLAS ｜ It's about 15,000 signatures from members of various Olympic sporting associations requesting that the gold medals for our Olympics are actually made of gold.

GINA ｜ Olympic gold medals aren't made from gold?

NICHOLAS ｜ No, they're made from silver.

GINA ｜ But we call them gold.

NICHOLAS ｜ Yes, that's right.

GINA ｜ Are you telling me that at Olympic ceremonies as currently performed there are two people on the podium with silver medals?

NICHOLAS ｜ That's right. They're made from silver but only one of them looks silver, the other one looks gold.

GINA ı Isn't there a legal problem here?

JOHN ı I think there might be.

NICHOLAS ı That's an interesting observation, Gina, but I'm sure it's one you'll find your way around.

JOHN ı We can't make gold medals out of gold. Have you any idea of what that'll cost? We're going to have to do this with Australian dollars. It costs a wheelbarrow of Australian dollars to buy a gold filling.

NICHOLAS ı Not at all. All I'm saying is that a problem that up until 30 seconds ago was the Minister's problem is now your problem.

JOHN ı And the Minister will be confronting this issue, will he, by his usual method of being photographed in a hard-hat pointing at a concrete mixer? Good grief!

John's last words are directed towards a Nicholas who has gathered all his climbing paraphernalia and walked off. In the meantime the sprinklers come on. John and Gina are in the path and are sprinkled.

GINA ı It just keeps getting better and better, doesn't it?

John and Gina are walking along a path.

JOHN ı I don't think that presents a major problem. If the gold medals aren't gold, we shouldn't call them gold. Call them the yellow medal.

GINA ı It doesn't quite have the same ring to it, does it? 'Triple yellow medallist Dawn Fraser.'

JOHN ı Well, no, it lacks mystique. And I can't imagine that the winner of the grey medal and the winner of the brown medal will be all that disappointed that they didn't get up for the yellow.

GINA ı Better to come fourth.

JOHN ı Yes, being run out in the heats is not looking like a bad result either. But I suggest that overall we avail ourselves of the Athens option.

GINA ı What's the Athens option?

JOHN ı You know, 'Whilst we were moved by the terms and the scope of your very interesting petition, we suggest you redirect your meritorious inquiries to the 2004 Athens Organising Committee whose schedule would appear to allow more time for appropriately serious and careful consideration of the many persuasive elements in your excellent proposal.' So you get the Athens option.

John screws up the petition into a ball and tosses it over the shoulder. The camera operator picks up the litter.

GINA ı I like the sound of that.

JOHN ı Yes, it's very good. The whole matter is solved. It never has to be revisited.

Saturday 10.46 p.m. Participants are in the lounge.

JOHN ı Have we heard anything about that transport strike?

GINA ı They're talking wildcat action.

JOHN ı When?

GINA ı If I knew when, it wouldn't be wildcat action. It would be 'exceptionally well-organised punctual cat action'.

JOHN ı Just when we've got the bloody IOC coming out here. Isn't that typical? Just what we need.

GINA ı Your obsession with the IOC is bordering on the unwell, John.

JOHN ı Tell that to the good folk of Atlanta.

BRYAN ı Are you going to come for a drink?

GINA ı I'll finish up, thanks.

BRYAN ı Katerina and I are just going to have a drink.

JOHN ı No, I think I'll push off too, thanks Bryan.

BRYAN ı Okay, well, we'll see you at the ropes course tomorrow. 6.30.

JOHN ı I beg your pardon?

GINA ı 6.30?

BRYAN ı Yes.

JOHN ı 6.30?

JOHN ı In the morning?

BRYAN ⏐ Yes.

JOHN ⏐ There's no such thing, Bryan. Where are we supposed to go?

KATERINA ⏐ You just have to go out to the verandah. There's a table with a folder on it. You register and out you go.

JOHN ⏐ At 6.30 in the morning?

BRYAN ⏐ Yes, I'm looking forward to it. I think it'll be great.

JOHN ⏐ It's hardly worth going to bed, Bryan.

GINA ⏐ Can we organise a wake-up call?

JOHN ⏐ I'll ring you at ten past six or something.

GINA ⏐ All right. Good night.

BRYAN ⏐ Good night.

JOHN ⏐ Good night.

BRYAN ⏐ Come on, John. Come and have a drink.

JOHN ⏐ No, I don't want a drink, thanks Bryan. I can't afford to have a drink anyway. I've got to get up at sparrow.

BRYAN ⏐ John, you are determined not to enjoy yourself.

JOHN ⏐ I'm not determined not to enjoy myself.

BRYAN ⏐ You are. You won't contribute. You won't participate. You're going to miss out on every benefit and experience there is in this place. John, come on. Open up your mind.

KATERINA ⏐ Great. Free up your thinking.

BRYAN ⏐ We're going to be out of here in a minute. You want to go back there refreshed and revitalised.

KATERINA ⏐ Renewed.

BRYAN ⏐ Renewed and all that stuff.

JOHN ⏐ Yes. I'll go and have a lie down, I think.

BRYAN ⏐ You think this is just bullshit, don't you? You do.

JOHN ⏐ You psychic now, too, are you Bryan?

BRYAN ı John, just give yourself a chance.

JOHN ı Yes, I'll do that Bryan. See you in the morning.

BRYAN ı Give yourself a chance.

JOHN ı See you in the morning. Goodnight. *(He leaves, passing the barman on the way out)* Two Scotches over there, I think.

KATERINA ı That's great, Bryan. That's great.

BRYAN ı Well, I think it's really important. Do you want a Scotch?

KATERINA ı Yes.

BRYAN ı Two Scotches, thanks. Doubles.

KATERINA ı That's great, Bryan.

BRYAN ı Yes, it felt really good. I just . . . they just don't get it. They don't get it.

On his way to bed, John walks along the verandah, approaches the table, picks up the biro next to the ropes course registration form and starts filling it in.

JOHN ı Do you know Gina's room number?

CAMERA OPERATOR ı 109.

JOHN ı Thank you. Night, night.

CAMERA OPERATOR ı Good night.

Sunday 6.59 a.m. A very sorry-looking Bryan turns up to register.

BRYAN ı Good morning.

MIKI ı Good morning. Just sign here, thanks. If you grab a pair of climbing gloves from just out here and go out down here, you'll find the instructors there.

BRYAN ı Have Gina and John turned up yet?

Miki checks the register and finds their names.

MIKI ı John Clarke and Gina Riley. Yes, they've been up bright and early. They must be on the course already. Yes. Bryan? *(His sense of direction is of some concern)* That way.

Cut to shots of Gina and John still asleep in their respective rooms.

Sunday 1.28 p.m. Gina and John are on the croquet lawn.

GINA ǀ So how do you play it again? Croquet?

JOHN ǀ Croquet. You hit the ball through the hoop and you end up hitting that stake. You do it using the grip I showed you earlier. Remember to follow through.

GINA ǀ I'll give it a burl.

Katerina and Miki approach while Gina has a shot. She hits the stake from a long way away.

MIKI ǀ John!

GINA ǀ What does that mean?

JOHN ǀ That means you win, actually, and I don't have a shot. I'll have a practice.

MIKI ǀ John. John.

JOHN ǀ Hello.

MIKI ǀ Can we speak with you?

JOHN ǀ Of course.

KATERINA ǀ John, you seem to be having a little difficulty handling the situation.

JOHN ǀ I'm not in any way trying to be critical. I think what you do here is probably of enormous value to many people and I have no objection, in principle, to coming up here and spending a weekend humming rather a lot and standing on one leg in the garden pretending to be a tree.

MIKI ǀ You were really good doing that.

JOHN ǀ Thank you very much. It's just that right at the moment I'm not in the right frame of mind to deal with make-believe problems. We have *real* problems.

BRYAN ǀ What problems?

John sees Bryan, shielding his eyes from the glare of the sun.

JOHN ǀ Hello, Bryan. I tell you one problem for a start. While you were a bit busy yesterday, Gina and I were visited by Nicholas who informed us that on Monday the IOC are coming to Sydney, Bryan, and I quote, 'to inspect all the venues'.

BRYAN ı Surely not all the venues.

JOHN ı All the venues, Bryan.

MIKI ı What's the problem with that?

JOHN ı Bryan will explain the problem with that.

BRYAN ı We haven't got all the venues.

JOHN ı That's right. You see, we don't need to imagine we're running the Olympics and we have problems. We *are* running the Olympics and we *have* problems.

KATERINA ı Didn't that man, the one who runs the Olympics — the Spanish guy, what's his name?

BRYAN ı Juan Antonio Samaranch.

KATERINA ı Didn't he say that Sydney's Games preparation was fantastic?

GINA ı Follow through, John. Yes, that's because there were no preparations.

JOHN ı Yes. He couldn't be wrong, you see. He also said 'I've never seen preparations like it.'

GINA ı He also said at the same stage at Atlanta there were virtually no preparations.

BRYAN ı And he said that the Atlantic Olympics was truly exceptional.

JOHN ı Are you all right Bryan?

GINA ı That was code.

MIKI ı The IOC talks in code?

GINA ı Oh yes.

JOHN ı Everything the IOC says is code for something else. If, for example, they describe the function that Bryan persists in calling 'the Atlantic Olympics' as exceptional, that's the equivalent of saying 'hand me a twig, please, I'd like to scrape the Atlantic Olympics off the sole of my shoe'.

BRYAN ı Yes, but he did then come out here and say that he was delighted with it all.

JOHN ı Why wouldn't he, Bryan? He had the three of us wandering around town with him explaining we were putting the finishing touches on everything.

GINA ı 'Finishing touches' is code.

JOHN ı That's right, 'finishing touches' is code for 'we've bought the concrete'.

John and Gina are in the gym. Gina is trying to reach a mechanical weight bar and John has somehow got himself on some kind of climbing frame for adults.

GINA ı John, we've got to stop moving the fencing venue.

MIKI ı Oh, there's fencing.

JOHN ı Oh yes, there's fencing all right. You don't often see fencing these days, do you? A drop of the old Errol Flynn. Swish, swish. You hardly saw him move. His opponent would be showered and dressed and halfway home before he realised his shoes were full of blood and he was dying.

GINA ı We've moved the fencing venue four times now. We put it in Darling Harbour and then they bumped it for the basketball. Then we lounged it in the Keating Pavilion but moved it for judo. It rested briefly at the Hordern Pavilion before it was moved for Greco–Roman wrestling. Seemed to have settled in nicely with the people at Moore Park before it was moved for administration space. Oh. I'm done.

JOHN ı Gina! I can't get down.

John is in the pool, Gina poolside, and Bryan, still looking fragile, is on a banana lounge.

JOHN ı Well, that's the problem.

GINA ı We could move the fencing back to the Keating Pavilion but where would the judo go?

KATERINA ı One venue short?

GINA ı Move the judo back and then what happens to the fencing?

BRYAN ı One venue short.

KATERINA ı Always one venue short.

JOHN ı Is repeating the problem with this religious devotion of some kind of beneficial psychological effect? It's not a heck of a lot of help to any rational process. We're trying to solve the problem.

KATERINA ǀ One venue short.

JOHN ǀ Are you mocking me?

GINA ǀ Oh, do Esther Williams again, John.

JOHN ǀ Esther Williams. Ladies and gentlemen, Esther Williams.

He leaps and dives in an attractive aquatic twirl combining the appeal of Hollywood and a practical representation of whales feeding.

KATERINA ǀ One venue short.

John and Gina are playing cards. Bryan looks on.

BRYAN ǀ Hey, would anyone miss the fencing if it wasn't on?

JOHN ǀ I like your thinking, Bryan, but I think you'll find we're obliged.

GINA ǀ If we chose the most obscure sport in the Olympics and simply didn't hold it, would anyone notice?

JOHN ǀ And you'd tell the athletes what?

GINA ǀ Sorry, venue burned down. Here's a bus timetable and some McHappy vouchers. Welcome to our beautiful city.

BRYAN ǀ Would anyone miss it?

JOHN ǀ That's an interesting question. If we selected a sport and just kind of disappeared it, is anyone going to notice?

GINA ǀ So the fact that fencing . . .

JOHN ǀ . . . to take a simple example . . .

BRYAN ǀ . . . wasn't going to be on.

JOHN ǀ Would anybody notice that? Would anybody write about it?

GINA ǀ It would be an enormous scandal in . . . Fenceland.

BRYAN ǀ Yes, but not here, which is the only thing of interest to us.

JOHN ǀ The IOC would be furious.

BRYAN ǀ How would they know?

In lounge room.

JOHN | Okay, what is the most obscure sport we've got?

GINA | Well, what the hell is this . . . Federation International D'escrime.

JOHN | D'escrime. Yes, that's pretty obscure. I've never heard of it. What's that?

GINA | I don't know. Escrime . . . escrime.

JOHN | Escrime.

BRYAN | What is it?

GINA | It's French obviously.

JOHN | Sounds French.

GINA | It'll be in the back here. Escrime. Escrime.

JOHN | Escrime. Escrime. *(In voice)* Get your tutsi-frutsi escrime. Get your tutsi frutsi. What is it?

GINA | Fencing.

JOHN | Fencing. Are you serious?

GINA | Escrime.

JOHN | If a tree falls in a forest. How long is that scheduled to run for? The escrime?

GINA | Nine days.

JOHN | Well, can't we reduce . . . Nine days for the escrime! Surely if you schedule from arsehole to breakfast you can bowl it over in three or something. Get rid of it.

GINA | You'll never fit it in.

JOHN | What do you mean we'll never fit it in? I'm not really planning to hold it at all. I'm just trying to come up with a schedule that's logical enough for the bloody Federation D'escrime.

BRYAN | John! John!

JOHN | What?

Bryan points to the documentary crew.

BRYAN | Camera.

JOHN ı They can't hear us. We're trying to make the schedule plausible so the Federation D'bloody escrime will sign off on it.

BRYAN ı But won't they want to have a look at the facilities beforehand?

JOHN ı Yes, of course they'll want to inspect the facilities. Every sport wants to inspect the facilities, Bryan. That's code.

BRYAN ı Code for what?

JOHN ı That's code for 'I want a free trip to Australia, please, and can I be driven past the venue of my choice at the speed of sound . . .

GINA ı . . . on the way to a five-star knocking shop for some pina colada and some horizontal rumba, Aussie style.

JOHN ı Exactly.

BRYAN ı If worse comes to worst I can always get my cousin to knock something up in fibro with an hour's notice.

JOHN ı I don't think the position's quite that serious, Bryan.

They are still in the lounge.

GINA ı Fun is over. Fun is definitely over.

BRYAN ı What's the matter?

GINA ı There's a copy of the full text of today's press conference. Listen to this: 'The IOC intends to undertake vigorous scrutiny of promises made by host cities. All host cities in the near future must adhere to all promises made with regard to the construction of event facilities and venues.' We are stuffed.

JOHN ı That's it. We're doomed.

GINA ı We're buggered.

BRYAN ı No, no, no.

JOHN ı Yes, we're buggered. It's all over.

BRYAN ı No, no, no.

JOHN ı Why?

BRYAN ı Wait a minute.

GINA ❘ No, we are, Bryan.

BRYAN ❘ No. That's code, isn't it?

JOHN ❘ How's that code?

BRYAN ❘ It's code.

JOHN ❘ Why?

GINA ❘ How?

BRYAN ❘ 'In the near future.' Isn't that code?

JOHN ❘ 'In the near future.'

GINA ❘ Oh, so it is!

JOHN ❘ 'In the near future.' Yes. That's a bit different, isn't it?

GINA, JOHN & BRYAN ❘ Athens!

A CONFLICT OF INTEREST

Friday 8.36 a.m. At the office. Gina's humming to herself while reading the paper and thinking aloud.

GINA ı What is that song? Oh God, John's not going to like this.

John walks in on cue.

JOHN ı John's not going to like what?

GINA ı Good morning.

JOHN ı Good morning. John's not going to like what? Come on, tell me. I take disappointment very well.

GINA *(Reading the paper)* ı All right. 'The dust has hardly settled on the scandal that toppled Sydney Olympic guru Steven Hitkicker before speculation has turned to the question of who might be his replacement.'

JOHN ı Whom.

GINA ı 'Word reaches this writer that eager for the position and attracting considerable attention is controversial Sydney businessman Joseph Williams.'

JOHN ı Get away. Coffee?

GINA ı Oh please.

BRYAN ı Joseph Williams? Is it true?

GINA ı Manny the Mouse's gossip column.

BRYAN ı It must be true.

John picks up a small radio.

JOHN ı Listen to this. Listen to this, here we go. Here he is on the radio. He's in the paper, he's on the radio. Go and flick the telly on, Bryan. See if Joseph Williams is on the telly. Listen to this. Are you listening? Now, I want you to watch something. *(He drops the radio in a glass of water)* Who wrote that rubbish, Gina?

GINA ı Manny the Mouse.

JOHN ı How did I know you were going to say that?

John is in his office, on his mobile phone.

JOHN ┃ Oh Manny the Mouse. All the news that's fit to flush.

Hello. Manny? John Clarke, how are you? Yes. Yes, it is about Joseph Williams, since you ask, Manny. I enjoyed your column today. Tell me, why have they got a photograph of your infant son at the top of it? It's not? Is it really? I didn't think photography was developed until about the 1860s.

Yes, well Joseph Williams bothers me considerably, Manny. Can I have a talk with you about . . . yes, Cafe Salmonella. I remember it well, yes. Half an hour, yes, I can probably do that. No, I can do that. Half an hour's fine, Manny. Thanks very much, no, good. I'll see you there.

(As he is walking out) I'll be about three hours, Gina. *(To receptionist)* If anyone rings I'll be back in about five minutes. Bryan, I'll be about an hour. If Joseph Williams gets on one more board in this city I think it'll be his eighteenth.

BRYAN ┃ That's still seventeen boards left that are prepared to live with him.

JOHN ┃ You make it sound like it's not a problem, Bryan.

BRYAN ┃ Is it a problem?

JOHN ┃ Let me outline the problem for you, Bryan. This man invented conflict of interest. He can't be interested in something without immediately recognising the problem he's going to have to deny he's got. But if you want to work for a man like that, Bryan, without knowing whether what you're doing is going to benefit the Olympics or some rort he's got going on the side, then I think the pair of you will probably get on like a bloody house on fire, Bryan.

BRYAN ┃ The point about this is he is a very well-respected business identity in this country. There was a feature article on him on Saturday in the paper.

JOHN ┃ Really? In the newspaper that he's on the board of was it, Bryan? Or the one that his construction company spends $15 million a year advertising in — arguably at a very slight discount. I'll be back in about an hour, Bryan.

BRYAN ┃ Say hello to Manny for me.

JOHN ┃ To who?

BRYAN ┃ Manny.

JOHN ┃ I didn't mention any Mannys, Bryan. I think you must have misheard me. I said I was going out.

John is in the cab, talking on his mobile phone.

JOHN ı Is there a limit to the number of boards a single human being can be on? Are they issued by the Franklin Mint as collectibles? All right. I'll ring him now. Bye. *(Finishes one call and punches the number to another. The phone beeps at him)* I beg your pardon. What do you mean 'no signal'? No signal. I'm at the centre of the universe. I'm at the epicentre of the known cosmos. No signal.

TAXI DRIVER ı Ninety-seven per cent coverage, those new phones.

JOHN ı Really? The other 3 per cent presumably consists of the central business district and a couple of outlying districts in which human beings live.

TAXI DRIVER ı Give it a shake.

JOHN ı Give it a shake. God, you've read the whole manual, haven't you? What page was that on? *(Phone beeps into life)* Hello. You're a genius. *(Into phone)* Michael Kroger, please. *(To taxi driver)* When we get there, can you just pull over on the left and I'll jump out. And can you wait for me?

TAXI DRIVER ı Right, okay.

JOHN ı Thanks. I won't be long. *(Into phone)* He's in an ABC board meeting? I'll wait.

John enters café. He is looking for someone.

JOHN ı Now where is he? There he is. Gidday.

Manny notices the documentary crew.

MANNY ı What's all this? The boy from the west made good?

JOHN ı *(To camera operator, waving the camera away)* Actually you can perhaps go down the end. I want to have a private conversation with Manny. I mean, no, right down the end. Go to about Albury. Private conversation. Keep going.

MANNY ı Well, you obviously read my column.

JOHN ı I did read your column, Manny. I was very impressed. I take it you'll be entering it for some kind of fiction award, will you? I know you get paid two hundred grand for writing this garbage every year, Manny, but do you actually write it or does SOCOG write it? Why isn't there a photo of SOCOG at the top of your column? You obviously don't write it. You just give this guy puff, after puff, after puff. I know something about Joseph Williams, Manny. *(He gets out some papers)* I'll show you something. Those are the boards he is on. That other page are his known share holdings. *Known* share holdings, Manny. Just put your hand over one eye and see if you can read me the top line.

MANNY ι What's your point?

JOHN ι The good news, Manny, is you're not going to need glasses. But I'm afraid the bad news is I think you might be facing the wrong way. I don't know why you keep giving this guy so much puff.

MANNY ι I print what comes in to me.

JOHN ι But he gives it to you. I'll tell you what he's doing. He's just going to be networking these Olympics. He'll just be using it for his own benefit on every front and he's using you.

MANNY ι All right, John. I'll tell you what, you can give me something . . .

JOHN ι I haven't got anything that would interest you, Manny.

MANNY ι Of course you have.

JOHN ι I haven't. You're in the gutter. My mind is on higher things.

Back at the office. Gina is scrabbling through her desk drawer for something.

BRYAN ι Gina, I don't know what John's worrying about. Nobody reads gossip columns.

GINA ι Everyone reads them.

BRYAN ι I don't know anyone who reads them.

GINA ι You don't know anyone who *says* they read them. It's the most read section of the newspaper.

BRYAN ι More than horoscopes?

GINA ι I don't know. I don't read the horoscopes.

BRYAN ι You *say* you don't read horoscopes.

Gina doesn't look well.

GINA ι Bryan, could you get me a drink of water, please?

BRYAN ι Yes, sure. Are you all right?

Gina looks frazzled and crawls under the desk for solace. Bryan walks in with a glass of water.

BRYAN ι Gina?

GINA ι I need a holiday. This job's killing me. Somebody offered me a seat on the bus this morning. Look at me.

BRYAN ι Nobody would mind if you went home a bit early.

GINA ι It's not the business hours, it's the after hours.

BRYAN ι What's the problem?

Gina gets up from under her desk.

GINA ι Can you tell me how it has become my job to show every blow-in from overseas the sights of our city? It never bloody stops. I've never known an event so capable of generating VIPs. As far as I can tell, the prerequisite for being a VIP in Olympic circles is that you wear aftershave and have a pulse.

BRYAN ι What did he want to do?

GINA ι Get drunk, see a strip show; for variation see a strip show, get drunk. A night out with Oasis would be a relief. Oh! *(She shudders)* Part of last night has just come back to me.

BRYAN ι Which part?

GINA ι The part involving the head of the Albanian Skeet Federation.

BRYAN ι Yes. And . . . ?

GINA ι And the possibility that I may have set fire to his toupee.

BRYAN ι What did you do that for?

GINA ι It was the only way I could think of to get at least one of his hands off me.

John is still in the car, attempting to have a conversation as his mobile phone cuts in and out.

JOHN ι Frank. Look, I know we haven't seen eye to eye on everything over the years, but we have to do something about this — keep Williams out of the Olympics. There must be a board in Sydney the guy's not on. Frank! Yes, Frank are you there? Yes, there must be a board he's not on, Frank. Frank, hang on I've lost you. Frank! Ah, got you back. Frank there must be a board . . . you know people, get a whole lot of numbers together. You've got to . . . Frank! Frankie! Frank, where are you?

(John speaks deliberately to the driver) Okay, my friend will get off at about this point. Thank you. *(He winds down the window and hurls the phone out into traffic. He then continues his conversation)* Frank! You're just as likely to hear me now. Frank, there must be a board in Sydney that Williams is not on. Ah yes, that's better. I can hear you now.

Meanwhile, back at the office, Gina is quaffing Berocca.

GINA ı And every one of the bastards wants to fly business class.

John happens to walk in at this point.

JOHN ı Which one of the limitless field of bastards are you referring to there?

BRYAN ı Visiting dignitaries.

JOHN ı Visiting dignitaries. Listen, I've made a decision. We are going to do everything humanly possible to keep Joseph Williams off our board.

BRYAN ı John, don't fight what you can't change.

JOHN । That's the ANZAC spirit, isn't it Bryan?

BRYAN । John, I'm just saying it's inevitable.

JOHN । It's not inevitable. He has a conflict of interest and I don't want to work here under those circumstances.

BRYAN । Just like your conflict of interest.

JOHN । I don't have a conflict of interest, Bryan. How do I have one?

BRYAN । Yes you do, John. If he gets on our board he's going to sack you.

JOHN । He's not going to sack me.

BRYAN । He's going to sack you because he hates you.

JOHN । Oh, don't be silly.

BRYAN । You hate him and everybody knows you hate him.

JOHN । Don't be silly, Bryan.

BRYAN । John, I think the world of you but you've got just as big a conflict of interest as he has.

Meantime Gina has crawled under her desk for solace again as the men carry on their discussion outside Gina's office.

JOHN । Gina doesn't look well. I don't. Do you know what a conflict of interest is?

BRYAN । Of course I do.

JOHN । It's an incapacity to reconcile responsibilities in one area, Bryan, with responsibilities in another. I don't have that and I very strongly object to his.

BRYAN । Keep digging that hole.

JOHN । The other thing I object to is I keep seeing him in the media. We've had Manny's puff piece, we'll have a feature thing in a broadsheet, in a minute he'll be on '60 Minutes' and his children will say what a wonderful father he is . . . I wouldn't mind it if it weren't so bloody obvious.

Gina runs past. John is surprised.

JOHN । What's wrong with her?

BRYAN ı Big night with the Albanians.

JOHN ı Really? She went out with an Albanian delegation. What does that mean?

BRYAN ı She set fire to one of their wigs.

JOHN ı Really? *(To camera operator)* Did you hear that? Gina went out last night with some Albanian delegation and set fire to some bloke's wig. She set fire to his wig . . . are you serious? That's a good effort, isn't it? No wonder she's a bit crook.

BRYAN ı Have you seen the price of casino stock this morning?

JOHN ı No, I haven't. Do you know the time?

BRYAN ı Ten-thirty. Two cents.

JOHN ı Two cents. Good time to buy, Bryan.

BRYAN ı Yes, as long as you don't buy that.

JOHN ı Yes, as long as you're not putting your money into something we spent $15 million buying at about $8.60.

BRYAN ı Have we got a meeting with the Americans?

JOHN ı Have you seen my file on Joseph Williams? Yes, the meeting with the Americans is still on.

BRYAN ı Do we have to work out this deal over the facilities?

JOHN ı Didn't you know you and I were going to get lumbered with doing this?

BRYAN ı I just hope we don't have to take responsibility for this.

JOHN ı I agree. It's not our idea, obviously.

BRYAN ı We wouldn't want to be anywhere near this, would we?

JOHN ı No.

BRYAN ı Aren't they just going to sell off all the sporting venues to foreign investors?

JOHN ı Yes, although that's not probably what they're going to call it.

BRYAN ı No, but that's what it is though, isn't it? It's just a big sell off of public property. The dollar is in the dunny. It's going to be a fire sale.

John finds the file he is looking for.

JOHN | There you go . . . Joseph Williams. It's all there, Bryan. Conflict of interest. Conflict of interest.

Yes, they're not going to call it a fire sale though, are they? They're going to call it 'Legacies for future generations'. 'Facilities constructed for the Olympics and now available for the edification and enjoyment of generations of kids for hundreds of years to come.'

BRYAN | What happened in Melbourne? What legacy did they have?

JOHN | As a result of the Olympics?

BRYAN | Yes.

JOHN | Slums, by and large. They built a whole lot of accommodation out at West Heidelberg. It's still there, I think. You still hear it mentioned from time to time. 'Police later found the vehicle abandoned at West Heidelberg.' 'Police are anxious to speak to the population of West Heidelberg.'

BRYAN | Are we going to fight this, John?

JOHN | This thing this afternoon? You bet we are. Can you get Ian Barrundi to come?

BRYAN | Ian Barrundi? Yes.

JOHN | Get him to come.

BRYAN | We'd need a weight lifter.

JOHN | Well, we need a recently retired, top flight international athlete.

BRYAN | Who's as thick as pig shit.

JOHN | He's very good in a meeting, Bryan. He's excellent in a meeting.

BRYAN | He knows nothing about corporate law and doesn't know what the Minister's deal is.

JOHN | The Americans don't know that.

BRYAN | It'll take me an hour and a half to brief him.

JOHN | He doesn't need to say anything. Go and ring him. He doesn't need to say anything. I just want him to be there. Tell him to dress for church and be in attendance.

BRYAN | Did the minister tell you what the deal is?

JOHN | Well, yes. He told me what he thought the deal is and he told me that he is expecting you and me to proceed the matter. I think he's hoping that we can get it done today.

BRYAN ı Does he realise we've got to keep control of the venues if we're going to get the Games on at all?

JOHN ı I don't think he thinks we're going to lose control of the venues in a properly phased privatisation programme with all the right checks and balances.

BRYAN ı That's serious.

JOHN ı It's very serious, Bryan, and we don't want it traceable back here. We don't want anything to do with it.

BRYAN ı But it *is* traceable back here.

JOHN ı It is at the moment.

BRYAN ı I mean, have a look. I have budgets, I have spread sheets, the whole thing.

JOHN ı Exactly. That is the difficulty.

BRYAN ı What do you want me to do?

JOHN ı I want you to get Ian to go to the meeting and I want you to come to the meeting and if I ask you anything in the meeting I want you to say 'I think there are some issues there, John'. And if money comes up I'd like you to say that 'we're waiting upon some valuations there, John'. I'll try to do the rest of it on a wing and a prayer. I just don't want us to get stuck with them.

BRYAN ı Neither do I.

Friday 2.07 p.m. John and Bryan are at the meeting with William T. Eyck, MBA, an international venue broker. The meeting has been going for some time. Coats are off. Ties are loosened.

WILLIAM ı Okay, so we commit $15.8 million to a joint marketing venture with the Sydney Olympic Games.

JOHN ı Yes, that's the proposal.

WILLIAM ı And then we would co-own — with the Sydney Olympic Games — the cycling Velodrome, naming rights to the two Olympic cycling venues, the Velodrome and the Time Trial track.

JOHN ı That's right, and then we would lease both those venues back from you.

WILLIAM ı We would have to be party to any plan to alter or vary that facility or any other cycling facility of that sort in the area.

JOHN ı Any other cycling facility. What about a road?

WILLIAM ı Well, any other cycling facility specifically used as a cycling facility.

JOHN ı You just want to make sure that you're going to get a return here.

WILLIAM ı That's right.

JOHN ı You've got a lot of money tied up here and you want to make sure you're going to do all right out of it.

WILLIAM ı Yes, we would have to have a secure income position, yes.

JOHN ı But if we saw someone somewhere else in Sydney riding a bike we wouldn't be obliged to put them in the back of a van and take them down to your facility and force them to pay to get in?

WILLIAM ı No.

JOHN ı No, that would be a bit much.

WILLIAM *(Realises that John is having him on)* ı Well, that'd be ridiculous.

JOHN ı That'd be ridiculous but you see my point, don't you? We don't want there to be any possibility whatever that you're not going to make a lot of money out of it.

WILLIAM ı We have a lot of capital tied up in it, yes.

JOHN ı That's exactly right, yes. I remember thinking exactly the same thing when the government was paying for it. Have you got the all-up costs there, Bryan? What did it end up costing?

BRYAN ı We're still waiting for some valuations.

WILLIAM ı Now, we need valuations of the facilities for depreciation purposes.

JOHN ı Yes, we can do that.

BRYAN ı I think there are some issues here, John.

JOHN ı I think we could probably do that. *(To William)* Have you got a valuation you'd like?

WILLIAM ı Oh no. We need a valuation from somebody who had the authority to make property valuations.

JOHN ı Yes. Independent. Qualified. Yes. I'll speak to me brother-in-law.

WILLIAM ı Cost to be borne by you.

JOHN ı Bryan?

BRYAN ı Yes, well, I think there are some issues there too.

JOHN ı I don't think that'll be a problem. I'm sure we can do that.

WILLIAM ı So I would come to you? Is that the way it would work?

JOHN ı Well . . .

WILLIAM ı No, it is you, isn't it?

JOHN ı Well . . .

WILLIAM ı See, you wouldn't actually be doing this, would you?

JOHN ı See, not me personally, no, sadly. The arrangement will be between your company and our parent organisation.

WILLIAM ı Who runs the organisation?

JOHN ı Well, ultimately the Minister.

WILLIAM ı There wouldn't be a change of Minister if there was a change of government?

JOHN ı No, you'd still be dealing with the Minister.

WILLIAM ı Yes, but it'd be a different Minister.

JOHN ı No. It would be the Olympics Minister.

WILLIAM ı It would be a different person.

JOHN ı Who would be a different person?

WILLIAM ı If there was a change of government, who would be running things?

JOHN ı The Minister would be running things . . . that's his job. He runs . . . He's the Minister for the Olympics.

WILLIAM ı So it wouldn't matter who the Minister was?

JOHN ı It never has so far, no.

WILLIAM ı So who is the Chief Executive?

JOHN ı At the moment?

WILLIAM ı What do you mean at the moment? How many have you had?

JOHN ı I'm speaking from memory . . . about four, so far.

WILLIAM ı What happened to the other ones?

JOHN ı Some of them are spending a little bit more time with their families.

WILLIAM ı Were they not well qualified?

JOHN ı Very well qualified indeed, yes.

WILLIAM ı Were they not doing a good job?

JOHN ı Doing an excellent job. They wouldn't have been in that position had they not been doing a very good job indeed.

WILLIAM ı So why aren't they there now?

JOHN ı No idea.

WILLIAM ı See, I don't understand how anybody would want to stay.

JOHN ⏐ Well, nobody has. That's the point I'm outlining for you.

WILLIAM ⏐ So does your board have a Chair?

JOHN ⏐ Yes, we have a Chairman. Actually the Chairman hasn't attended the last couple of board meetings. It's fair to say that the board is in a touch of strife just at the moment.

WILLIAM ⏐ What kind of strife?

JOHN ⏐ They've invested rather a lot of money in the Tamagotchi Company in Burma.

WILLIAM ⏐ Why did they do that?

JOHN ⏐ To raise more money for the Games.

WILLIAM ⏐ What was the problem?

JOHN ⏐ There's a bit of a problem with the Tamagotchi Company in Burma.

WILLIAM ⏐ How much did they lose?

JOHN ⏐ The Chairman would have a record of all that. Unfortunately he is currently away.

WILLIAM ⏐ Where is he?

JOHN ⏐ He's in Burma.

WILLIAM ⏐ Why?

JOHN ⏐ He's on the board of the Tamagotchi Company up there.

WILLIAM *(Laughing)* ⏐ How am I going to explain this to my board?

JOHN ⏐ Your board is aware that you are dealing with Australians on this one?

WILLIAM ⏐ How soon do we have to, you know, make this thing happen?

JOHN ⏐ Oh, as soon as possible. 'Get this thing done as soon as possible'. Those were certainly my instructions.

WILLIAM ⏐ I think I should consult with my people. Maybe we could meet again some time next week?

JOHN ⏐ I was rather hoping that we could proceed pretty quickly with this. We've come here prepared to do this deal today. We've got the corporate legal adviser, we've got the deal memo, you've got the money. Let's boogie.

WILLIAM ⏐ You see, I think there are some issues with the structure of the deal.

JOHN ⏐ Bryan?

BRYAN ⏐ I agree.

JOHN ⏐ Ian?

BRYAN ⏐ He agrees.

WILLIAM ⏐ I think we need some more time.

JOHN ⏐ I think if you feel that, perhaps what you ought to do is you write a letter to the Minister explaining that we've had these negotiations in the spirit of friendly goodwill and from your point of view, there are certain aspects of the structure of the proposed arrangement that concern you. You'd like to go and see the Minister with your people and can he get back to you about arranging that meeting?

WILLIAM ⏐ That's sounds fine. We'll do that.

JOHN ⏐ Let's do that. That's a good idea. Now, Darling Harbour. Are you familiar with Darling Harbour?

WILLIAM ⏐ Yes.

JOHN ⏐ Yes. Because we could put a bike track in there. That's got beautiful views. It's a lot more central.

BRYAN ⏐ I think there are some issues there.

IAN ⏐ So do I.

Sunday 9.16 a.m. Camera crew arrives at John's front door. He is asleep.

JOHN ⏐ It's Sunday, what the hell is . . . Oh! This is the weekend we're doing the 'what we're like at home' thing. I thought that was the 22nd. Well, hang on a minute. I'll just open the door again. *(Shuts door)* Are you going to knock? Can you knock? Do it again. You knock.
　　　　(There is a knock on the door) Who is it?
　　　　(John opens the door again. This time he is very perky indeed) Hi there! How are you? Come in. Where have you been? I've been up since about five. Come in. *(He turns and we follow him, observing his patriotic sleepwear, which features the very attractive green and gold colours and has the name of the country, STRAYA, emblazoned across the back)* Have some coffee or something. Round here to your right. I was just having a bit of sort of old, relatively unreconstructed breakfast. It's a bit pre-war; the bacon, the eggs, the toast, the tomatoes. Probably the National Heart Foundation's sponsorship's up in smoke but there you go. Man can't really live at this

speed, can he? *(He notices a number of Guinness cans lying about)* The Guinness was probably left there by the Meals on Wheels people, I think.

I'm actually through here *(Leads the crew into another room)* reading the paper so come in here. I mean, you won't be able to use any of that anyway. Just give us a minute and . . . do I look all right? Start the camera in five . . . you'll put music over this won't you? . . . four, three, two, one.

(He narrates his own documentary) Sunday morning finds Clarke sitting on freckle reading paper as he does every week, scampering through the news, such is his dedication. Here we go . . . Soapie Star Fights Bulimia . . . smart money is probably on bulimia there. Here's the main thing though — front-page story. Joseph Williams — you can back him in can't you? 'Businessman's secret charitable donations. Joseph Williams tells of his little known secret million-dollar deal to benefit philanthropic causes.' 'Secret' . . . 'tells of' 'secret' . . . 'tells of' 'secret' . . . 'tells of' 'secret' . . . 'tells' 'secret'. I give up — spot the deliberate mistake. Does the man think we're absolute idiots?

CAMERA OPERATOR ⏐ What are you going to do about it?

JOHN ⏐ Oh what can you do about it? It's his standard method. He seems to be able to get pretty well anything in the pap . . . *(Phone rings)* Just excuse me, there's a phone ringing somewhere. There it is. Excuse me.

(He continues to provide his own voice-over) Grabs phone. Sticks same up to ear.

Speaks into same. Hello. Absolutely. Did you see that? Does he think we're insane? *(Knock on door)* There's a film crew here, now there's someone knocking at the door. Hang on. *(To camera)* Bruce, can you get that? Hang on, there's someone coming. Does the man think we're absolutely stupid? I'd better go actually. There's someone at the door. I'll ring you later.

Bruce opens the door to find Gina holding the same paper. She is not pleased in any way.

GINA ⏐ What are you doing here?

CAMERA OPERATOR ⏐ Just doing the background footage.

GINA ⏐ Is John here?

JOHN ⏐ Who is it?

GINA ⏐ It's me.

JOHN ⏐ Oh yes. It's the 'what we do in the weekends' thing.

GINA | I thought that was on the 22nd.

JOHN | So did I. They're actually going to your place next. You'd better go home or you won't be there when they arrive.

GINA | Have you seen the paper?

JOHN | Yes. Does Joseph Williams think we are complete idiots?

GINA | Not that crap on the front. *(She reads from another section)* Listen to this, it says here that I set fire to an Olympic VIP's wig. Bryan was the only person I told about that. I'm going to bloody kill him.

JOHN | Yes, I reckon that's a bit rugged. I reckon telling Bryan something in confidence and then finding it in Manny's column — that's a bit rich.

GINA | I didn't say it was in Manny's column.

JOHN | Is it . . . is it in Manny's column?

GINA | How did you know it was in Manny's column, John?

JOHN | Is it in Manny's column? I haven't . . .

GINA | How did you know it was in Manny's column?

JOHN | I haven't even got to Manny's column. What page is Manny's column? It's in Manny's column, is it? *(He finds it. By now Gina looks very uncharitable)* So it is.

Gina stomps off.

JOHN *(To camera)* | Might be better if you duck around to Bryan's first.

Monday 8.21 a.m. At the office.

BRYAN | Morning. *(To camera)* Did you film at John's place on the weekend?

CAMERA OPERATOR | Yes.

BRYAN | Nice house, John's. Yes. Early Tornado. What did he do then?

CAMERA OPERATOR | Then he went to church.

BRYAN | Church? What, him? John Clarke. Our John Clarke? You've got to be kidding. He hasn't been to church in his life. I don't think he's even driven past a church. Couldn't have. *(To John)* Good morning.

JOHN ı Good morning.

BRYAN ı Surprise. *(Bryan indicates the crew)*

JOHN ı Good morning. Oh my God, they're always here, aren't they? I mean, how would you be if everywhere you went, there I was, all ready with a camera pointed straight up your eyeball? Bryan?

BRYAN ı Yes.

JOHN ı How many bloody episodes of this series have we done? About ten or something. You'd think the novelty would wear off, wouldn't you, but oh no.

BRYAN ı Gina wasn't all that impressed with the gossip item.

JOHN ı Yes, she intimated that to me in broad terms, Bryan. I don't think anyone will read those things anyway. No one reads Manny's column.

BRYAN ı Are you serious? I've had 27 messages on my answering service including one from the National Wig Company . . .

JOHN ı I'd ring them back.

BRYAN ı . . . re potential Olympic sponsorship. People read it. I read it.

JOHN ı No, no one reads it.

BRYAN ı It's true. By the way, church on Sunday, John?

JOHN ı To some extent, Bryan, yes.

BRYAN ı Anything on your mind?

JOHN ı Oh you know, just Joseph Williams. I'm just going to read about him, no doubt. *(He begins to open the paper)*

BRYAN ı He's in there.

JOHN ı Of course he's in here, Bryan. It's illegal to produce a newspaper in this state if you don't have Joseph Williams in it somewhere.

BRYAN ı He's on the front page.

JOHN ı Front page. I won't even read it. That is it. I give up. That is it. 8.23 Monday morning: John officially gave up. Retired to pavilion looking tense but dignified. What's he done now, Bryan? Has he got a papal knighthood? Is he hosting the 'Midday Show'? No, he's won the Nobel Prize for Physics, has he?

BRYAN ı No.

JOHN ı Got runner-up in the Miss NSW contest?

BRYAN ı Shot by girlfriend's husband.

JOHN ı I beg your pardon?

BRYAN ı Shot by girlfriend's husband.

JOHN ı Shot?

BRYAN ı Dead.

JOHN ı Shot by girlfriend's husband. Girlfriend's . . .

BRYAN ı . . . husband.

JOHN ı Girlfriend's husband. Conflict of interest, Bryan.

BRYAN ı Conflict of interest, John.

JOHN *(To camera)* ı What did I tell you?

TRANSPORT

On his way to work, John is visiting the construction site of an important Games facility. He enters the site office to speak to Harry Gibbs, the site foreman.

JOHN | Gidday. How are you?

HARRY | Gidday

JOHN | I'm John.

HARRY | Gidday. Harry Gibbs.

JOHN | Bloody cold, isn't it?

HARRY | I'll say. I had to break the dog off the tree this morning.

JOHN | That's pretty good, though. *(Pointing to the wood-burning stove)*

HARRY | It's not bad, is it?

JOHN | It's a bloody ripper.

HARRY | We haven't got much in it today.

JOHN | It's pretty warm.

HARRY | Yes, well we usually have it up to about there *(He indicates a point on the stove)* but we had it up to here *(A higher point)* yesterday.

JOHN | That must have chucked out some heat.

HARRY | Oooo yes. You couldn't get in here yesterday. Do you want a cup of tea? *(He holds a mug of tea)* I've just made one.

JOHN | No, I'll be right, thanks. I just had one. You go ahead.

HARRY | You haven't seen a pencil about, have you?

JOHN | Pencil. What sort is it?

HARRY | It's a red one. HB. Just short of a good length. I had it here a minute ago.

JOHN | No. I've got a biro if you want.

HARRY | Oh good on you. Thanks. *(He takes the biro and stirs his tea)*

JOHN | So how are things going here?

HARRY | Pretty good. We're a bit behind with the weather but we'll get there.

JOHN ı Are you on schedule?

HARRY ı Well, we are with this part of it, yes.

JOHN ı What part of it aren't you on schedule with?

HARRY ı We're a whisker behind with that section out there. *(He points out the window. John looks)*

JOHN ı Oh yes. What's that?

HARRY ı That's the diving pool. Look. Here it is here. *(Points to the plan)* See? Diving pool.

JOHN ı Why is it out there? *(John points out the window)*

HARRY ı That's where it is on the plan. That's the basis we work on here at the Institute.

JOHN ı I don't know that that's where it is on the plan, is it?

HARRY ı Yes it is.

JOHN ı Hang on. Isn't it supposed to be out here? Look at this.

HARRY ı Where? No.

JOHN ı What's it doing out there? Where's your drainage?

HARRY ı Under the deck. It's all done. Look, look, look. *(Points to the plan again)* Here it is here. See?

JOHN ı Yes, but isn't this your drainage here? I mean, isn't that your drainage running along there?

HARRY ı It can't be. You see all that concrete out there?

JOHN ı Yes.

HARRY ı That concrete base out there?

JOHN ı Yes.

HARRY ı Well, that's where the diving boards are going.

JOHN ı And who put that concrete in?

HARRY ı We did.

JOHN ı Why did you put it in out there?

HARRY | Because that's where the diving pool's going.

JOHN | Yes. How do you know that?

HARRY | Why would they have a diving pool in a different spot from the diving boards?

JOHN | Hang on. Are we both agreed that from the edge of that pool to that boundary is a distance of 63 metres?

HARRY | Yes. That is exactly 63 metres from that pool.

JOHN | It can't be.

HARRY | Well, go out and measure it.

JOHN | Look, are we saying the same thing? Are we saying that from the edge of that pool to that boundary there is 63 metres?

HARRY | Yes. That's why we put it there.

JOHN | OK, show me the boundary. That could be part of the problem. That is a different distance along the front there.

HARRY | Hang on.

They bend lower and look more intently at the plan. In the background we hear races on the radio. The race finishes.

HARRY | Who got second?

JOHN | Hagen's Pride, I think. *(He points to the plan)* See? That is a different distance along there. That's not the same. That is totally different. Somebody shifted the boundary and why has it got Education Department on this one and not on that one?

Wednesday 9.42 a.m. Gina is in Nicholas Bell's office.

GINA | Aren't we doing the transport? I thought we were doing it?

NICHOLAS | No, you're going to help but we've actually set up a new body to run it. The Olympics Road and Transport Authority.

GINA | ORTA.

NICHOLAS | No, we *have*. It's happening. We're going to do it . . .

GINA | No, no . . . Sorry. ORTA. That's their name.

NICHOLAS ꟾ What?

GINA ꟾ As in 'Why I orta. . .'

NICHOLAS ꟾ I'm sorry. I don't know what it is you're talking about. It's called O.R.T.A. The point is that they are responsible to the Minister.

GINA ꟾ The Transport Minister?

NICHOLAS ꟾ No, the Olympics Minister.

GINA ꟾ Do they have any contact with the Transport Minister?

NICHOLAS ꟾ No, this is our show.

GINA ꟾ Yet they're obviously working in the transport area.

NICHOLAS ꟾ Of course they bloody are. They are the Olympics Road and Transport Authority.

GINA ꟾ But they have no contact with the Transport Ministry.

NICHOLAS ꟾ No, they won't need to be involved with the Transport Ministry.

GINA ⏐ How are they going to organise the transport then, if they're completely independent of the Transport Ministry? I mean, who's going to actually do the work?

NICHOLAS ⏐ City TransWorld. There's a big pow-wow with them the day after tomorrow with your people as well.

GINA ⏐ Who are City TransWorld?

NICHOLAS ⏐ They're an international transport consultancy. The point is, we're trying to get them to come on board at the moment and help us with the set-up and maintenance of the transport infrastructure.

GINA ⏐ What's the matter with the public transport system?

NICHOLAS ⏐ Nothing. We'll still be using the public transport system, only these people will help with the set-up and maintenance of the infrastructure.

GINA ⏐ What does that mean?

NICHOLAS ⏐ Look, these are the real hot shots in this field at the moment and we are very pleased with them. The Minister is very concerned about costs, as you know.

GINA ⏐ Oh these people are going to be cheaper, are they?

NICHOLAS ⏐ Yes, we believe so.

GINA ⏐ Have you see their figures? I mean, how are they going to do it?

Nicholas flicks through the document.

NICHOLAS ⏐ Here we are. Look. We believe economies can be achieved in these areas by redesigning the infrastructure.

GINA ⏐ What does that mean?

NICHOLAS ⏐ Look, the Minister is very happy with these people. You're going to meet them the day after tomorrow. They're top guys. We think they're going to do a good job.

GINA ⏐ What have they done before?

NICHOLAS ⏐ They are experts in transport infrastructure for major events. This is what they do.

GINA ⏐ Well, what about Bryan?

NICHOLAS ⏐ Bryan?

Nicholas's phone rings. He answers it.

GINA ı Bryan has set up the entire transport model.

NICHOLAS *(To Gina)* ı Well if this goes through . . . *(To phone)* Sorry . . .

GINA ı Yes. Have you spoken to the Minister about this?

NICHOLAS ı Bryan will be fine. Yes.

GINA ı What do you mean Bryan will be fine? What does that mean?

NICHOLAS *(Into phone)* ı Sorry, hang on. *(To Gina)* Bryan will get a package. Bye.
Read the brochure. *(Into phone)* Yes. Yes. *(Once Gina is out of room, he puts down
the phone)* Yes. Yes. Yes. Yes.

*Wednesday 1.25 p.m. Bryan is talking to Bella Saulwick from Games
Technology Support.*

BRYAN ı If we could work that out we could work out where to warehouse the parts.
The transport's going to be all over the place.

BELLA ı Where are the parts now?

BRYAN ı The parts are in Pyrmont.

BELLA ı That place up behind the bridge?

BRYAN ı Yes, but if a bus breaks down in Pittwater it's going to take us half a day to
get the spares up there. If we could put a diagnostic unit inside a vehicle, could we
get it to send a signal back to some central point?

BELLA ı So you want to fix the problem before the bus breaks down.

BRYAN ı Exactly. Do it overnight. Do it in down time. But we'd need the diagnostic unit
to send the signal back to some central point. Can we do that?

BELLA ı Now, that is an idea I've never heard of.

BRYAN ı I've never heard of it either but it's worth having a crack at, isn't it?

Bryan hands Bella a small piece of machinery.

BELLA ı This is the unit that the sensor transmits to, is it?

BRYAN ı Yes.

BELLA ｜ And this is in the vehicle.

BRYAN ｜ Yes.

BELLA ｜ Well, you need to stick a transmitter in here somewhere. I don't know how powerful it would need to be.

BRYAN ｜ Well, it just needs to reach a mobile transponder.

BELLA ｜ Oh really? You've got a deal with Telstra?

BRYAN ｜ There's a bloke in their Operations Division. I used to work with him on the railways.

BELLA ｜ That's probably not impossible. Just leave it with me, Bryan.

BRYAN ｜ I will.

Bryan walks out of the office as Bella starts fiddling with the sensor.

John is walking down a corridor when he meets Gina.

GINA ｜ Oh hello.

JOHN ｜ Hello.

GINA ｜ Where have you been?

JOHN ｜ I've been to the swimming and diving complex.

GINA ｜ How was it?

JOHN ｜ Very difficult to say.

GINA ｜ Why?

JOHN ｜ I don't know yet. There's some problem out there. Did a bloke from the Rowing Federation ring me with regard to some electronic starting gates or something?

GINA ｜ I don't think so.

JOHN ｜ Good. I must have given him the wrong number.

GINA ｜ Have you heard of a mob called City TransWorld?

JOHN ｜ City TransWorld? Yes. Dimly. Aren't they some consultancy outfit they've got to come in and talk about the transport arrangements or something? Didn't we get something about this? *(He rifles through the papers he is carrying)* Yes, there. We did.

GINA ⏐ What transport?

JOHN ⏐ Transport for the Games.

GINA ⏐ The whole thing?

JOHN ⏐ Yes, I suppose so.

GINA ⏐ Well, what about Bryan?

JOHN ⏐ What about him? He'll be working with them, won't he?

Gina quickly scans the document John just handed her.

GINA ⏐ Have you read this?

JOHN ⏐ No.

GINA ⏐ Have you told Bryan about it?

JOHN ⏐ No.

GINA ⏐ This is Bryan's job.

JOHN ⏐ Really? Are they going to get rid of Bryan?

Wednesday 2.18 p.m. Gina is in her office. She is on the phone, engaged in official-sounding business.

GINA ⏐ Hello, it's the Olympics Office here, your transport proposal for the Games . . .

RECEPTIONIST *(Enters to give Gina her messages and points to a stack of paper)* ⏐ London on line 1 and this is urgent.

GINA ⏐ Right. *(Back to her phone call)* I need you to fax me the cost estimates for that. No? I must warn you the Minister might take a very dim view of your withholding this information. What is your name please, because I may have to report you . . . my fax number? 9947 0993. No. Thank you. *(Hangs up, triumphant)* Yes.

Wednesday 7.14 p.m. John and Nicholas are in a pub.

NICHOLAS ⏐ What sort of delay?

JOHN ⏐ I don't know but the diving pool — to some extent at the moment — is in completely the wrong place.

NICHOLAS ı What do you mean it's in the wrong place?

JOHN ı It's supposed to be over here and it's over there.

NICHOLAS ı Does it actually matter?

JOHN ı Yes. It can't be over there. The soil is corrosive out here. We did soil tests all over that area. It won't last two years if we stick it in out there. It's in the wrong place.

NICHOLAS ı Why the hell was it put in the wrong place in the first place?

JOHN ı I don't think they've actually done anything wrong. I've got a feeling the dimensions of the land have changed.

NICHOLAS ı Why?

JOHN ı I don't know. That's why I want your help.

NICHOLAS ı I'll see what I can do. I'll see you.

Nicholas ups and leaves.

JOHN ı Thank you.

CAMERA OPERATOR ı Why didn't you mention Bryan to him, John?

JOHN ı Look, just shoot stuff, will you, Bruce? Leave me alone. I've got enough to worry about without you being judgemental. I will. I'll pick the moment.

Wednesday 7.56 p.m. John wanders back into the office.

GINA ı Oh, you're back.

JOHN ı I am indeed. Good evening.

GINA ı Good evening. How was Machiavelli?

JOHN ı He wasn't bad. I just had a drink with him. There's some cock-up with the dimensions of the land up at the diving complex. I just want them to realise it's got nothing to do with us.

GINA ı Has Bryan spoken to you?

JOHN ı No. About this transport thing?

GINA ı Yes.

JOHN ı No.

GINA ı They're going to shaft him, you know.

JOHN ı Do we know what they're actually going to do? Have we seen the transport plan?

GINA ı I think they want to break up the public transport system after the Games and this is the way they're going to do it.

JOHN ı Why do you think that?

GINA ı Because I've been sniffing around the NSW railway system. The Minister's put valuers in. Why else would he do that?

JOHN ı How do you know the Minister's put a valuer in?

GINA ı You know that guy, Lismore?

JOHN ı No, I don't think I know a Lismore, do I?

GINA ı You know, friend of Bryan's, works at the railways. He said they've had valuers in all week.

JOHN ı I don't think I know a Lismore, do I?

GINA ı Yes, you do. You know, red-headed guy?

JOHN ı Oh yes. Comes in here a bit.

GINA ı Yes. His real name's Barry or something.

JOHN ı Why is he called Lismore?

GINA ı Well, his hair is the closest thing you can get to Orange. The next station to Orange on the NSW rail system is Lismore.

JOHN ı That's nice isn't it? *(He looks down towards Bryan's office)* Is that Bryan's light on? Is Bryan still here? Is he still there?

John walks out of his office and heads for Bryan's office. He sees Bella there instead.

JOHN ı Oh, hello. Haven't you got a home to go to?

Bella is holding a piece of paper. She is smiling.

BELLA ı This is brilliant.

JOHN ı Well, it's nice to see people happy in the service.

BELLA ı You know Bryan, don't you?

JOHN ı Yes, I do know Bryan.

BELLA ı Has he told you about this diagnostic thing he's setting up?

JOHN ı No.

BELLA ı We are going to be able to run permanent checks on every bus in the metropolitan transport system. So rather than waiting for things to break down we'll just fix them in the down time.

JOHN ı Will it work?

BELLA ı Well, he's had his little units in 50 transit authority buses. He's got a separate maintenance team . . . he hasn't had a single breakdown.

JOHN ı None at all?

BELLA ı Not one.

JOHN ı How did he get his little units into 50 buses?

BELLA ı I don't know.

JOHN ı He's good, isn't he?

Bella nods in agreement.

Thursday 9.28 a.m. John is in Nicholas's office. Nicholas is displeased.

NICHOLAS ı Someone from your office rang City TransWorld yesterday and asked for a cost schedule, is that right?

JOHN ı Do you mean did it happen?

NICHOLAS ı Of course I mean did it bloody happen.

JOHN ı Is there a problem with that? How are we supposed to drive a budget if we don't know what the thing costs?

NICHOLAS ı The point is, what are your people doing ringing them demanding this information? It'll be in the profile of the project.

JOHN ı Well, when are we going to *get* the profile of the project?

NICHOLAS ı You'll get it soon. Very soon. Look, it's a very professional bunch we're dealing with, John. Let's not be stupid. I mean, these three blokes, they're top people. Did you know each one had an MBA?

JOHN ı Is that right? Are they MBAs in transport though, or are they MBAs in remembering the names of people they went to school with?

NICHOLAS ı Do you know who it was who made that call?

JOHN ı Yes, I do. Yes. And he did it on my specific instructions.

NICHOLAS ı It was a woman.

JOHN ı Ah well, that is serious. Oh yes, I can see the concern there. That's actually dangerous. I'm surprised that's allowed. A woman?

John lets out a whistle, indicating the gravity of the position.

Gina pays a visit to the Corporate Affairs Office and approaches the counter where she is served by Daphne.

GINA ı Oh hello. I was wondering if I could get the details of the directors of these companies.

DAPHNE ı Yes, we can do that for you. They're all in Transport, are they?

GINA ı Yes, I think so. Do you have a search engine that could tell me the other interests of those people?

DAPHNE ı Yes, we do.

GINA ı Fantastic. Let's have a play with that too.

Thursday 2.10 p.m. Bryan's in a parking lot talking to Bella on the mobile. He has his car rigged up. Bella is back in the office, looking at the diagnostic of Bryan's vehicle on her computer.

BRYAN ı Okay, here we go. Right, off you go.

BELLA ı Right indicator. *(Bryan flicks the indicator on. On Bella's screen, the right indicator is shown as blinking)*

BELLA ı And left. Brakes. *(Bryan flicks the indicator on. On Bella's screen, the left indicator is shown as blinking)*

BELLA ı Headlights. *(Bryan flicks the headlights on. On Bella's screen, the headlights are shown as beaming)* Okay. That all works.

BRYAN ı Great. Okay, do you want to try one?

BELLA ı Yes.

BRYAN ı Okay, let's do it. *(He gets out of the car and lifts the bonnet)* Off you go.

BELLA ı Yes. *(The computer scans and picks up an error in the car)* Brake fluid is low.

BRYAN ı *(He checks the brake fluid. It is low)* Very good.

BELLA ı Front brake pads are worn.

BRYAN ı I'll have to take your word for that. Yes. All right. Good.

BELLA ı Fuse gone somewhere — looks like the heater.

BRYAN ı Hang on a second, I'll have a look. *(He gets back in the car and checks)* Geez, you're right. I didn't even pick that up myself. Well done. *(He gets out of the car again)*

BELLA ı Bryan . . .

BRYAN ı Yes?

BELLA ı Door.

BRYAN ı Oh, sorry. *(He shuts the car door)* All right, see you later. Well done.

Bryan hangs up and talks to the camera operator.

BRYAN ı I think this is going to work. She is good. She is very good. She is excellent.

Gina is back at the office. She is on the phone.

GINA ı Yes, the fax arrived. Thank you, Daphne. Now, what's a trust? Right. So now I have to find out who the trustees were. Is that . . . you've got them there? Yes, I would. Thank you Daphne. Thank you very much. *(Hangs up the phone)* Whoo oooo!

John walks into her office.

JOHN ı Gidday.

GINA ı Hello.

JOHN ι Have you got the Media Accreditation stuff here somewhere?

GINA ι Just putting the finishing touches on it.

JOHN ι Have you done the press release on the Internet?

GINA ι Yes. Got that covered.

JOHN ι Have you booked the satellite for the CNN thing next week?

GINA ι Got a call in.

JOHN ι Did you fax Juan Antonio's itinerary out here next week . . .

GINA ι As we speak.

JOHN ι . . . because there's a message on the machine saying that they haven't got it.

GINA ι Bloody hell.

JOHN ι Do you think perhaps we could fax it again? You do know they should actually have had it yesterday?

GINA ι I'll take that on board, John.

JOHN ı Gina, have you actually done any of these things at all?

GINA ı No, I haven't. *(Hands John a note pad with her notes on it)* Look at the names of the people who run City TransWorld.

Gina ushers the camera operator out of her office and shuts the door.

GINA ı Just out here. Thank you.

Thursday 6.07 p.m. Daphne drops in Bryan's office.

DAPHNE ı Hello.

BRYAN ı Daphne!

DAPHNE ı Bryan!

BRYAN ı How are you?

DAPHNE ı Oh, how lovely.

BRYAN ı Nice to see you. How's Tom?

DAPHNE ı You know Tom.

BRYAN ı What's been going on?

DAPHNE ı Well Bryan, I've been doing some work for Gina.

BRYAN ı So you said on the phone.

DAPHNE ı Yes. It's okay to come to you?

BRYAN ı Of course it is.

DAPHNE ı Well look, I've been going through . . .

Friday 9.42 a.m. Nicholas and John greet guests for the Transport Meeting as they file into John's office.

NICHOLAS ı *(To guests)* Good morning. Come on in.

JOHN ı *(To guests)* Good morning. Nice to see you.

Bryan comes in.

NICHOLAS ⎪ Hello, Bryan. Good to see you.

JOHN ⎪ Gidday, Bryan. How are you? *(To Nicholas)* Have you spoken to him?

NICHOLAS ⎪ No, I haven't. Have you?

JOHN ⎪ I think you probably should. No. How could I? What would I say to him? I haven't been told anything.

NICHOLAS ⎪ Does he know about these people?

JOHN ⎪ I don't know what he knows, Nicholas.

NICHOLAS *(To guests)* ⎪ Hello. Good to see you. Good morning.

JOHN ⎪ I think you owe him an explanation.

NICHOLAS ⎪ I don't think I do. *(To guests)* Thank you very much.

JOHN ⎪ Do you know who owns City TransWorld?

NICHOLAS ⎪ What do you mean, 'who owns City TransWorld?'.

JOHN ⎪ I think you should look into that. *(To guests)* Good morning.

A bigshot approaches.

NICHOLAS ⎪ Sam. Welcome. Come on in.

JOHN *(To Sam)* ⎪ Hello there.

SAM ⎪ Good morning.

JOHN ⎪ Welcome to our humble home.

In the outer office, Gina gets off the phone as Bella leaves something on the desk.

GINA ⎪ Oops, got to go, sorry. Hi.

BELLA ⎪ Can I leave this grant application here for John?

GINA ⎪ Yes. Is it urgent? He's actually in a meeting.

BELLA ⎪ No. He just needs to fill in the details.

GINA ⎪ Grant application? What's that for?

BELLA ၊ The Education Department has some money available so maybe we can get it for Bryan's project.

GINA ၊ Oh great.

BELLA ၊ Do you know about Bryan's project?

GINA ၊ No. Is it good?

BELLA ၊ Yes, it's brilliant.

Sam Neill, the CEO of City TransWorld, addresses the meeting in John's office. He has very slight indigestion but controls it beautifully.

SAM ၊ Thank you all for coming. You probably know why we're here. We're looking at getting in on the transport infrastructure for the Games. We'd very much like to work with you people *(Slight indigestion, controlled beautifully)* and we're very excited about this at City TransWorld. We think that we have a good deal to offer you and we think that you . . . *(Slight indigestion, controlled beautifully)*. So perhaps if I could go through some of the elements of some of the sort of things that we'd be looking at doing and then maybe we could open it out for discussion after that? Can I ask first up if anybody here has any experience at all in the transport area?

John raises his hand.

JOHN ၊ Yes, Bryan worked for 27 years for the railways and ended up in charge of metropolitan services.

SAM ၊ The railways.

JOHN ၊ Yes.

SAM ၊ Well, you see, that's a very old-fashioned way of thinking right there. Nowadays it's all about integration of services and we'll be wanting to look at the complete transport picture. Now, the public transport system is obviously going to have to be augmented by other units. There will be a formula for all of this. *(Slight indigestion, controlled beautifully)*

And it'll be controlled by a computerised central point so that we will know where all of these units will be at any one time. *(Slight indigestion, controlled beautifully)* We're going to want to have a very close look at the Los Angeles Games and how the public transport system worked there because we see this as being the primary model for Sydney. We'll be looking at its weaknesses, we'll be looking at its strengths and we'll be looking at the lessons there for all of us.

NICHOLAS ı Can I ask a question?

SAM ı Nicholas.

NICHOLAS ı Thank you. John, can I ask what work has been done up to this stage by your people on this question? You see, what I am thinking is there may be a detailed study already undertaken on the Los Angeles public transport system and how it worked for them at the '84 Games. That sort of thing would give us a lot of information. Is that available at all?

JOHN ı Bryan?

BRYAN ı No.

NICHOLAS ı It hasn't been done at all?

JOHN ı Bryan?

BRYAN ı No.

NICHOLAS ı Is there a reason for that?

JOHN ı Bryan?

BRYAN ı They don't have a public transport system in Los Angeles.

Nicholas is slightly wounded but recovers quickly.

NICHOLAS ı Well, all right. Okay, Bryan. What work has been done on this? You see, I was at the Equestrian Centre the other night and where are we with that sort of thing? I mean, do we know how many buses we'll need to move 14,000 people from the finals of the dressage back to the city at one o'clock in the morning?

BRYAN ı 200.

JOHN ı Nicholas?

NICHOLAS ı Well, 200, 300, 400, yes. But do you know where we're going to get them from?

BRYAN ı We've already got them.

SAM *(Retrieving the situation)* ı Now, a lot of Sydney's transportation is actually done on the water.

NICHOLAS ı Yes, I'd say the majority.

SAM ⏐ So we'll need to acquire quite a few new craft. Does anyone know exactly how much of Sydney's transportation is done by sea?

NICHOLAS ⏐ I'm not sure but if it is the majority I think that's a good place to start from.

SAM ⏐ Bryan?

BRYAN ⏐ About 9 per cent.

JOHN ⏐ Cup of tea anyone?

Friday 3.17 p.m. Bryan walks into Gina's office with a bunch of flowers.

BRYAN ⏐ You know that Bella from upstairs in the computer centre? *(Gina looks up)* She is something.

GINA ⏐ Yes, they say she's very smart.

BRYAN ⏐ I gave her a problem on Monday and she's already done it.

GINA ⏐ Really?

BRYAN ∣ Yes. Very impressive. I asked if it was possible to send a signal from a diagnostic unit in a vehicle to a central database using a transponder?

GINA ∣ Oh yes?

BRYAN ∣ Yes, and of course you've got to have the phone line to go from the unit to the transponder, so guess what she does?

GINA ∣ I don't know.

BRYAN ∣ She has a better idea. She does it the other way round. She sends a signal from the transponder to the unit. And ask me what technology she uses?

GINA ∣ I don't know.

BRYAN ∣ She invents it. She invents it! On Monday she's got a problem, this afternoon she's demonstrating an entire new system she's figured out in two days. Amazing. You know what she's done? She's put a receiver chip inside the diagnostic unit and initiates the signal from this end. It bounces the information off the transponder, runs a check on the vehicle and of the computer in there.

GINA ∣ And that's good?

BRYAN ∣ Good? It's fantastic!

GINA ∣ Oh good. Good.

BRYAN ∣ People are bloody marvellous, aren't they?

GINA ∣ Some of them are, yes.

Bryan leaves Gina's office.

GINA ∣ Bryan, you've left your flowers here.

BRYAN ∣ Oh no. They're actually for you.

GINA ∣ What?

BRYAN ∣ I just wanted to thank you for helping me this week.

GINA ∣ My help? What did I do?

BRYAN ∣ I've got a friend, Daphne, who works at the Companies Office. Used to work in the railways together. Thanks.

Sam and John are having a cup of tea in the office together.

SAM ı John, I was thinking we might be able to find a use for . . . what's his name?

JOHN ı Bryan.

SAM ı Bryan. We could probably give him something. Seems to know his stuff.

JOHN ı Oh yes. He's very good, Bryan. He's terrific. Didn't you find him impressive?

SAM ı So how do we go about this? Would we approach him or would you talk to him? How do you want to do this?

JOHN ı I don't know. I've never offered a man his own job before. It might not be the easiest thing to do.

SAM ı In what way?

JOHN ı Well, he might, for example, take the view that he's already doing his own job.

SAM ı No, what I'm saying is, if we got the transport contract, we might be able to give him a job. It might be a break for the guy, you know.

JOHN ı What would he be doing?

SAM ı Well, he'd be helping us with the transport arrangements.

JOHN ı Yes, you'd need someone to do that. I can see that.

SAM ı You don't like us very much, do you?

JOHN ı That's a very old-fashioned way of thinking.

Friday 7.16 p.m. John and Nicholas are in John's office.

NICHOLAS ı There's been a bit of a hold put on the transport plan.

JOHN ı Oh yes. This is this City TransWorld business?

NICHOLAS ı Mmm. Might not be the best way to go. We're thinking about it. The Minister's very conscious of the need to go with someone with a solid and proven record in the transport area.

JOHN ı And what was the problem with City TransWorld?

NICHOLAS ı Nothing at all.

JOHN ı Did you have a look at that information I gave you?

NICHOLAS ı Yes. I just think that the Minister feels that perhaps there are people here just as well qualified to do the job.

JOHN ı Arguably more qualified.

NICHOLAS ı Exactly.

JOHN ı Incidentally, Bryan tells me that he put in an application for an increase in safety staff on the railways two years ago.

NICHOLAS ı That's a very good idea.

JOHN ı Hasn't even got a reply from the Transport Minister.

NICHOLAS ı Well, now might be a good time to have another look at that.

JOHN ı A very good time to *announce* it, I thought.

NICHOLAS ı Where?

JOHN ı Saturday's paper, for example. A lot of voters read that. It's their money. They might be very pleased to see it put to some sensible use.

NICHOLAS ı I think the Minister might smile on such a proposal if carefully put.

JOHN ı Well, I'll leave it with you then. Just try and remember, when you're carefully putting it, not to mention the Aquatic Centre because we wouldn't want it to leak out that there's a cost over-run down there of $1.3 million that's got absolutely nothing to do with the project, would we?

NICHOLAS ı No.

JOHN ı Which, incidentally Nicholas, while we're up this way, is not money that is coming out of our budget, is it?

NICHOLAS ı Fair enough.

JOHN ı It's not, is it?

NICHOLAS ı No. Good night, John.

JOHN ı Good night, Nicholas.

Nicholas leaves John's office.

NICHOLAS ı Good night, Gina.

GINA *(Calls out)* ı Good night, Nicholas.

NICHOLAS | Good night, Bryan.

BRYAN *(Leaving also)* | Good night, Nicholas. Good night, Gina.

GINA *(Calls out)* | Good night, Bryan.

BRYAN | Good night, John.

JOHN *(Calls out)* | See you, Bryan.

GINA *(She is leaving. She calls out)* | Good night, John.

Bryan and Gina leave.

JOHN *(He calls out)* | Good night, Gina.

John leaves.

JOHN *(To camera)* | Good night.